ADDITIVES

John Clark
Consultant : Jane F. Griffin

HarperCollins*Publishers*

First published by HarperCollins *Publishers* 1991
© The Book Creation Company Ltd 1991
Reprint 10 9 8 7 6 5 4 3 2 1

ISBN 0 00 458992 0

Printed in Great Britain by
HarperCollins *Manufacturing* Glasgow

Contents

Introduction

The Gem Guide to Natural and Artificial Food Additives is an easy-to-use pocket reference book. It provides an accessible and comprehensive guide to the wide variety of additives encountered in the modern diet.

All additives at present permitted for use in the UK are included and they are entered under their chemical names, in alphabetical order. The additive number and any alternative names are given in brackets after the headword. If it is necessary to look up a substance by its E number or permitted number, a quick-reference table in Appendix III (at the end of the book) gives the chemical name under which it may be found and its main function.

The entries explain the nature and composition of each additive, what its function is, the foods in which it is most commonly used and in what circumstances and by whom it should be avoided (i.e. hyperactive children or asthmatics).

Ingredients that are commonly used by manufacturers, such as modified starch, hydrolysed vegetable protein and glucose syrup, are also included. Entries on common foods and drinks give the additives and ingredients most likely to be found in them.

Preparing more food in the home will reduce the amount of additives in the diet. However, there are still some additives (e.g. salt) even in home-cooked foods, and this book will explain what they are and what alternatives may be used instead. There are entries on the main nutrients and some dietary information is provided, where it directly relates to additives. For more information on nutrition and diet, readers are recommended to consult the *Gem Guide to Healthy Eating and Nutrition* and the *Gem Calorie Counter*.

The foods and drinks are entered under their common names, and not under manufacturers' brand names. The book is thoroughly cross-referenced, and cross-references appear in **bold lettering**.

What is an Additive?

According to the 1984 Food Labelling Regulations, an additive is 'any substance, not commonly regarded or used as food, which is added to, or used in or on, food at any stage to affect its keeping qualities, texture, consistency, appearance, taste, odour, alkalinity or acidity, or to serve any other technological function in relation to food, and includes processing aids in so far as they are added to, or used in or on, food.' Many food additives are natural substances, while others are synthesized. A synthesized additive may be nature-identical (i.e. although man-made it has the same chemical composition as the natural substance) or

vi

artificial (i.e. it has a different chemical structure from any naturally occurring substance).

There are several substances that might be defined as additives which are not included, certainly for the purposes of food labelling. These substances include vitamins, minerals and other nutrients when they are used to fortify or enrich foods, or to replace nutrients that have been or will be lost, e.g. during processing or storage. Herbs or spices when they are used for flavouring are not considered as additives, but they would be if their function in the food was to add colour, e.g. curcumin (E100). Hops, salt, yeast or yeast extracts, malt or malt extracts, starter cultures (e.g. milk-souring organisms in cheese-making), air and water are not considered as additives either.

There are some additives that fall outside the control of the Food Labelling Regulations and therefore do not have to be declared. Any additive which is present in food because it was added to animal foodstuffs, or was used in a process or treatment carried out in farming or storage (e.g. pesticides, fumigants, sprout depressants or medicines) will not be declared on the label. This is of great concern to many consumers, and several groups and organizations are working to get this changed.

Why Do We Need Additives?

Additives have an enormous range of functions, but these functions can be broadly divided into four categories:

Additives that Keep Food Fresh, Stable and Safe These are preservatives and antioxidants; many foods would not be safe to sell without the use of such additives.

Preservatives prevent the growth of microorganisms that would otherwise cause food decay or health hazards, e.g. bacteria and moulds. Preservatives extend the shelf life of a product and the length of time it remains good once opened. Many of them are simple chemicals, often mild or weak acids such as acetic acid (found in vinegar) or sorbic acid (found in some fruits, but usually made synthetically). Other preservatives, however, are more powerful and complex chemicals and their extensive use has been questioned, such as the nitrates and nitrites used in meat products and sulphur dioxide, which is used in a wide range of products. (See individual entries for more information.) In most cases a specific additive is most effective in a specific product. In the UK there are over 30 permitted preservatives and the major ones include benzoates, sulphur dioxide, nitrates and nitrites and propionates.

Antioxidants prevent or inhibit the decay of food which occurs when food is exposed to the oxygen in air. They stop foods containing fat or oil from going rancid, which would result in unpleasant odours and flavours. They also prevent enzyme browning which can cause discoloration of fruit, vegetables and fruit juices. The antioxidants used in fats include the gallates, BHT (butylated hydroxytoluene) and BHA (butylated hydroxyanisole). Natural antioxidants include vitamin C in fruit and vitamin E in vegetables. These can be extracted or synthesized and used in food products, e.g. vitamin C in fruit drinks to stop the browning effect. Antioxidants, like preservatives, extend the shelf life of products.

Additives that Improve the Texture and Consistency of Food These are emulsifiers, stabilizers, thickeners and gelling agents. Emulsifiers combine substances that do not normally mix together into an emulsion. They are needed to incorporate air into liquid (e.g. ice cream), fat into water (e.g. artificial cream and salad cream) and water into fat (e.g. margarine). Emulsifiers also have other functions: preventing fruit particles from collecting together in fizzy soft drinks; slowing down the staling process in bread; preventing sugar from crystallizing out of chocolate and causing 'bloom' on the surface.

Stabilizers are used to stop the emulsion or mixture from separating. The physical properties of food may need to be varied in many ways, so thickeners and gelling agents are used, either separately or with emulsifiers. In the home the traditional thickener is starch, but starch presents the food manufacturer, who wants products with good shelf lives, with technical problems. It has a strong flavour, which can mask other ingredients, it requires heat to thicken and can form a hard 'set', which separates on storage or when a product is frozen. Alternative thickeners are therefore used, many of which are derived from natural sources, e.g. alginates, guar gum and carageenan. Modified starches are also used as thickeners, but at the moment their use is not controlled by law.

There are over 50 emulsifiers, stabilizers, thickeners and gelling agents permitted in foods and, depending on the amount used, many can be employed for more than one function.

Additives that Improve the Appearance and Taste of Food These are colours, flavours, sweeteners and flavour enhancers.

Colours and flavours are added to food and drink for a variety of reasons. The colour or flavour of a food may be lost during processing and storage and have to be replaced. The colour and flavour of the ingredients may have to be reinforced so that the final product does not appear paler and taste weaker than expected. Manufacturers seek uniformity of product from one batch to another and the controlled use of colours and flavours helps to achieve this, particularly when there are variations in the colour and flavour of the ingredients used. Colour and flavour are also added to foods which otherwise would be virtually colourless or bland-tasting, e.g. jellies.

Many of the colours found in natural foods can be extracted and used in food production, such as carotenoids (found especially in carrots), chlorophylls (green plant pigment) and anthocyanin (found particularly in red-, blue- and violet-coloured plants). For economic reasons manufacturers prefer to use nature-identical colours rather than the more expensive natural extracts.

The majority of the artificial colours are 'coal tar dyes', so called because they were originally made from coal tar, but are now synthesized from petroleum. Caramel, derived from glucose and other sugars, is the most commonly used individual colour; over 90% of all colouring matter in food is caramel. The solely cosmetic use of colours in foods has been increasingly questioned, and there are now many products which contain natural rather than artificial colour, and others with no added colour at all.

Although flavours make up the largest group of additives they have not been allocated 'E numbers'. A natural flavour may be a single chemical or it may be a complex blend. For example, 42 different chemicals make up the flavour of orange oil. Flavour chemists create the blends of natural essences and synthetic chemicals to flavour foods. The mixtures are often very complex combinations of chemicals, but on the ingredients list they only have to be declared as 'flavourings'.

Sweeteners include many sugars and hydro-lysed starches as well as artificial sweeteners, which are various chemical compounds found to have sweetening properties. Artificial sweet-eners can serve a valuable purpose by produc-ing the sweetness of sugar without the calories. They are used particularly in low-calorie and diabetic products. Because some of these sweeteners are so much sweeter than sugar, the desired sweetening is achieved with a much smaller amount, which can provide technical advantages.

Flavour enhancers (e.g. monosodium gluta-mate) do not have a characteristic or distinctive flavour, but they have the ability to bring out the flavour of other ingredients.

Miscellaneous Additives in Foods These include a number of different classes of addi-tives such as acids, bases and buffers. These are used for a range of purposes: to control the acidity or alkalinity of food; anti-caking agents to ensure free flow, e.g. dried milk and table salt; anti-foaming agents to prevent or disperse frothing, e.g. in juices during processing; glazing agents to produce a protective coating or a polish or sheen on the surface of a food, e.g. confectionery. Many of these additives can be described as processing aids, that is they are used to help manufacture the product rather than having a function in the finished product. However, some have dual functions. For example, the anti-caking agent magnesium carbonate is used in table salt to improve its flow during manufacture, but it remains in the salt and continues its function in the end product.

Food Labelling and E Numbers

The Food Labelling Regulations (1984) require that most pre-packed food must include a complete list of ingredients and this must include any additives are present. The additives are listed by their category, e.g. colouring, preservative, etc., and (except for flavours) this must be followed by the specific name or E number.

E numbers are a practical method of coding additives for countries in the European Community. Numbers and letters rather than names are easier to recognize, and so the importing and exporting of foods is made easier. Additives that appear on the UK permitted lists have a serial number allocated to them. If that additive is permitted throughout the EC it is given the E prefix. Additives with a

number but no E may be on the permitted lists
of some but not all of the EC countries, or alternatively they may be under consideration by
the EC. Additives allocated E numbers can be
natural, nature-identical or artificial. Certain
additives may have more than one use, but the
E number system groups classes of additives
together by their main function: E100-180
colourings; E200-297 preservatives; E300-321
antioxidants; E322-500 emulsifiers and stabilizers; 500-578 acids, bases, anti-caking agents
and other miscellaneous additives; 620-637
flavour enhancers and sweeteners; 900-927 miscellaneous additives.

Are Additives New?

During the 1980s there has been increasing
concern about the possible effects of additives
on our health. Although the concern is about
the use of modern chemicals, it should not be
forgotten that our food has never been entirely
free from additives.

Chemical substances, such as salt, sugar,
vinegar and alcohol, have been added to food
since ancient times. In particular, salting and
smoking were often essential for survival,
making it possible to store food against the
likelihood of periods of scarcity. One of the
earliest methods of preserving food, especially
fruit, meat and fish, was to dry them in the sun.
The removal of water inhibits the growth of

microorganisms, which prefer moist environments. One of the factors that made cereals such vitally important items in the diet of humans was their naturally low water content, which meant that they could be stored for long periods. The primary concern was always to preserve food, but even during Roman times additives were used for cosmetic purposes. Potash was added to wine and natural soda to vegetables to enhance the colour. The additives we use today may not all be desirable, but overall our methods of food preservation have greatly improved.

Food irradiation is the latest development in preservation, at least for certain foods. The advantages of irradiation are that it increases shelf life and reduces storage problems by inhibiting sprouting and ripening, controlling infestation and reducing the microorganisms that cause spoilage or food poisoning. For example, irradiation would eliminate *Salmonella* from poultry and fish. The extensive use of irradiation would also mean a decreasing use of preservatives.

However, the prospect of irradiated food has caused concern over four main issues. First, whether the process makes the food radioactive. In fact it does, but only slightly and for a very short time. When the ionizing radiation passes through the foods some atoms absorb it and become radioactive, but this is quickly lost through radioactive decay. Second, that the texture and taste of the food can change, making it less palatable. There may be some need to use additives to mask or control unpleasant flavours. Meat, eggs and dairy produce are particularly prone to these changes. It is not yet understood how these changes occur, but they limit the foods that can be irradiated. Third, that there is no way for the consumer to recognize nor a reliable test to establish whether a food has been irradiated. This has raised concern that old food items could be sold as fresh. Finally, there are fears that the nutritional content of food will be affected. Certainly vitamins C, B_1 and E are all at risk and essential fatty acids may also be damaged.

When food irradiation becomes available in the UK, it is hoped that it will be clearly labelled so that consumers can make informed choices, and those that wish to can avoid such food.

acceptable daily intake (ADI)   The amount of a particular substance that can be eaten by a person each and every day of his or her life without any harm. ADI is stated in milligrams per kilogram (mg/kg) of body weight.

An ADI can be given for a substance only if sufficient is known about its effects on the body or about what happens to it when it is absorbed by the body. This knowledge usually requires a considerable amount of scientific investigation.

There are no government-provided ADIs in the UK, except in the case of preservatives. Otherwise, the most authoritative ADIs covering a large range of additives are provided by the Joint World Health Organization/Food and Agriculture Organization Expert Committee on Food Additives. They give a full ADI when they are confident that enough research has been done. They give a temporary ADI when they feel that further research is needed.

acesulfame-K (also called **acesulfame potassium**)   An **artificial sweetener**, related to **saccharin**, that is about 200 times as sweet as sugar. It is more heat stable than saccharin and can be used in cooking. It is used in soft drinks, desserts and low-sugar jams and jellies. It has a bitter aftertaste and is often used in combination with other sweeteners. Acesulfame-K has no calorific value and no known harmful effects, although there are some controls on its use in the UK; for instance, along with some other sweeteners, it may not be used in ice cream. It is not permitted in nine other European countries nor in the US.

acesulfame potassium   Alternative name for **acesulfame-K**.

acetic acid (E260; also called **ethanoic acid)**   The acid in vinegar, in which its concentration is 4–6%. It can also be made synthetically. In vinegar, acetic acid is formed by the action of bacteria on the alcohol in wine, beer (to produce malt vinegar) or cider. A mixture of 5% acetic acid in water is sold to be used like vinegar, and is known as non-brewed condiment.

   Acetic acid, in the form of vinegar, is used as a preservative – many foods can be preserved by pickling them in vinegar. It is also a common ingredient of fruit and savoury sauces. Manufactured acetic acid has a number of purposes as a food additive. It may be used to add vinegar-like flavour, it is used in bread-making to inhibit the growth of mould, and is an ingredient of some processed cheeses. It is also employed as a **diluent** for certain colours and in the brewing of beer.

acetic acid ester of mono- or diglycerides of fatty acids (E472a; also called **acetylated**

mono- and diglycerides; acetoglycerides; complete and partial glycerol esters) A member of a versatile group of **esters** that are used as **coating agents**, **emulsifiers**, lubricants, **solvents**, **stabilizers** and **texture modifiers**. They occur in artificial cream, margarine and potato snacks. They may be produced from animal sources and are therefore not suitable for some vegetarians and certain religious groups.

acid A substance defined chemically as one that reacts with an **alkali** (or a **base**) to form a salt. In food, acids are added to give an acidic taste (e.g. lemon juice, vinegar). They are also used for the chemical action of the acid, which may involve such properties as affecting the way in which jam sets or preventing the growth of mould. Acidity in foods can be controlled using **acidity regulators** or **buffers**.

acid blue 3 Alternative name for **patent blue V**.

acid brilliant green Alternative name for **green S**.

acid calcium phosphate Alternative name for **calcium tetrahydrogen diorthophosphate**.

acidity regulators A group of substances used to control the acidity of a food, usually during manufacture. They include weak **acids** (e.g. acetic acid, fumaric acid, malic acid) and salts of such acids (e.g. various acetates, citrates and lactates). Some of these are also **buffers**.

acid sodium pyrophosphate Alternative name for **sodium dihydrogen diphosphate**.

acid yellow 17 Alternative name for **yellow 2G**.

ACP Abbreviation of acid calcium phosphate (**calcium tetrahydrogen diorthophosphate**).

ADI Abbreviation of **acceptable daily intake**.

adipic acid (355; also called **hexanedioic acid**) An organic acid used as a **buffer** and **raising agent**. In the latter application it is preferred to tartrates and phosphates because it does not absorb water. Adipic acid is also used to impart an acid taste to drinks, jellies and sweets. It occurs naturally in beet juice and is made synthetically from cyclohexanone.

aerating agent (also called **aerator**) A substance added to lighten the texture of food, such as a **raising agent** used in breads and cakes, or to gasify a drink, e.g. carbon dioxide gas dissolved under pressure in carbonated soft drinks and canned and bottled beers.

aerosol cream A cream packaged in aerosol canisters which is heat treated at very high temperatures to preserve it. Aerosol creams contain propellants so that the cream can be expelled from the container. They may also contain **gelling agents** and **stabilizers**.

aflatoxin A highly poisonous, carcinogenic substance produced by fungi of the *Aspergillus* group, which sometimes grow on rice, peanuts and other foods stored in a warm, moist atmosphere.

agar (**E406**; also called **agar-agar**; **Japanese isinglass**) A jelly-like substance extracted from certain types of red seaweed, employed as a **gelling agent**, **humectant**, **stabilizer** and **thickener**. It is also used in brewing to coagulate and precipitate proteins and tannins from wort, the sweet, brown liquid produced when malt is mashed with warm water. Technically, agar is a type of carbohydrate called a polysaccharide (as are cellulose and starch). It is used in a wide range of foods, from icing, ice cream and frozen custard to canned roe and the clear jelly with certain canned meats. It cannot be digested and large quantities may cause flatulence (it is used medicinally as a laxative).

aji-no-moto Alternative name for **monosodium glutamate**.

5

albumin (also called **albumen**) Any of a group of water-soluble **proteins** that occur in the blood and in certain foods, e.g. eggs and milk. They coagulate when heated, which is why the white of an egg sets when cooked.

alcohol (also called **ethyl alcohol**; **ethanol**) An organic liquid produced naturally by the fermentation (using yeast) of any substance containing sugar, such as fruit juice, wine or beer. Alcoholic drinks contain from a few per cent alcohol in beers up to 50% or more in strong spirits and liqueurs. Alcohol is toxic and addictive, in limited quantities it causes intoxication and in large quantities coma and even death. It is used as a **solvent** for various food additives and as a preservative, e.g. for fruit.

alcoholic drink In addition to **alcohol**, alcoholic drinks may contain various other ingredients and additives, such as **sulphur dioxide** as a preservative and **carbon dioxide** as an **aerator**. Nutrients are usually added to 'feed' the yeast during fermentation and **sorbic acid** to kill off the yeast after fermentation. In wines proteins may be used to clarify and mild alkalis to reduce the acidity. Other alcoholic drinks contain colouring matter such as **caramel**, which is commonly used in beer and whisky.

All alcoholic drinks are permitted additives, but because drinks containing more than 1.2%

of alcohol (by volume) do not have to have the ingredients listed on the label, there is no way of knowing what they are. This is of particular significance to people with **asthma**, in whom sulphur dioxide can trigger an asthma attack.

ale   See **beer**.

alecost (also called **costmary**)   A composite plant that originated in Asia, so named because its fragrant, bitter-sweet leaves were once used to flavour beer. It is still used as a seasoning, particularly in stews or casseroles of game, chicken or veal.

alginate   A salt of **alginic acid**. Permitted alginates include **ammonium alginate**, **calcium alginate**, **potassium alginate** and **sodium alginate**.

alginate ester (E405; also called **propane-1, 2-diol alginate**; **propylene glycol alginate**)   An **ester** of **alginic acid** extracted from brown seaweeds, employed as an **emulsifier**, **thickener** and **solvent** for flavours. It is used in ice cream, processed cheese and salad dressings. Alginate ester is also used to stabilize the foam head on beer and lager.

alginic acid (E400)   An insoluble substance extracted from brown seaweeds, employed as a

7

food additive (usually in the form of an **alginate**) for more than 50 years. It is used mainly in puddings, desserts and other sweet foods.

alkali A soluble **base**, which is a substance defined chemically as one that reacts with an acid to form a salt. Mild alkalis include **ammonium hydrogen carbonate**, and **sodium hydrogen carbonate**, used in foods to reduce acidity or to react with an acid to generate carbon dioxide gas (see **aerating agent**; **raising agent**). Other alkaline food additives include the carbonates of ammonium, calcium, magnesium, potassium and sodium; the corresponding hydroxides are also sometimes used.

allergen A substance foreign to the body that triggers an allergic reaction in a sensitive person. Different people are susceptible to different allergens, e.g. household dust, animal fur or hair and pollen. Less than 10% of allergic reactions in adults are due to food, although **food allergy** is more common in children.

allergy Hypersensitivity to a substance (**allergen**) that causes the body to react when it comes in contact with that substance. See **food allergy**.

allspice (also called **Jamaican pepper**; **pimento**) A flavouring that resembles a mixture of cinnamon and nutmeg, made from the seeds of a tropical American tree of the myrtle family. It is used to flavour pickled and preserved meats and may also be added to cakes, biscuits and puddings.

allura red (129) An **azo dye** once employed as a red **colouring** agent, which produces a skin reaction in some sensitive people. Its use is now banned in the EC and several other countries.

alpha-aminoglutanic acid Alternative name for **L-glutamic acid**.

alpha-carotene (E160a) An orange-yellow **colouring** agent that occurs naturally in carrots, oranges and tomatoes but is mainly made synthetically. It is also extracted from red palm oil. Alpha-carotene is used to colour butter, margarine, cheese and milk products, soups and cakes. It is converted to vitamin A in the body.

Alpha-carotene is permitted in foods described directly or by implication as being specially prepared for babies and young children. The maximum content of total added colour is limited to amounts consistent with its use as a vitamin source.

alpha-cellulose (E460b; also called **powdered cellulose)** A natural form of cellulose with a wide range of uses as an **anti-caking agent**,

9

bulking agent and **thickener**. It is found in ice cream, high-fibre bread and artificial cream. It is also employed, together with **isinglass**, to clarify beer because it causes suspended particles to flocculate and settle out of solution.

alpha-tocopherol, synthetic (E307; also called **vitamin E)** A synthesized form of vitamin E, employed as a vitamin supplement in flour, margarine and white bread. It is also used as an **antioxidant** in meat pies and sausages. It does not survive freezing. Synthetic alpha-tocopherol is not permitted in food intended specifically for babies or young children.

aluminium (E173) A silvery metal employed, as the only alternative to real silver, to coat cake decorations and dragées (the only use for which it is permitted). There is some evidence of a link between the presence of aluminium in the body and Parkinson's disease and **Alzheimer's disease**.

Aluminium is present naturally in many foods, particularly cereals and vegetables. Only a small amount is obtained from aluminium cooking pots because of the protective, stable layer of aluminium oxide. However, this layer can be corroded by salt (in cooking water) and natural acids in fruit and vegetables.

aluminium calcium silicate (556; also called **calcium aluminium silicate)** A mineral employed as an **anti-caking agent** in icing sugar and salt.

aluminium potassium sulphate (also called **potash alum; potassium aluminium sulphate**) An **acidity regulator, buffer** and **firming agent**, used in cheeses, flour and pickles. It is also used to clarify sugar, and may be found in foods containing sugar.

aluminium silicate Alternative name for **kaolin**.

aluminium sodium silicate (**554**; also called **sodium aluminosilicate**) A mineral that occurs naturally but is also synthesized, employed as an **anti-caking** agent in such products as icing sugar, powdered milk substitute and salt.

Alzheimer's disease A degenerative organic disorder of the brain. The disease impairs the memory, causes speech disorders and premature ageing. Its symptoms resemble those exhibited by sufferers of senile dementia, but Alzheimer's disease can occur at any age. The exact causes are unknown, but there is considered to be a link with accumulations of **aluminium** in the brain.

amaranth (**E123**; also called **red 2**) An **azo dye** used as a purple-red **colouring** agent (e.g. in

11

blackcurrant products, jams, fruit pies, soft drinks and trifles). It has been associated with **hyperactivity** in children and is banned in six European countries, the USSR and the US; its use is severely restricted in France and Italy. It should be avoided by people with **aspirin sensitivity** or **asthma**. Amaranth is also widely used in other products including toothpaste, medicines and cosmetics.

American mustard A mild, sweet yellow mustard, made from alba mustard seeds and flavoured with sugar and vinegar or white wine. It is used extensively in the US on hot dogs and hamburgers.

amidated pectin (E440b) A **gelling agent** and **thickener**, useful for producing jams and jellies that contain little sugar, made by treating **pectin** with ammonia. It is also used as an **emulsifier** and **stabilizer**.

aminoacetic acid Alternative name for **glycine**.

amino acid (also called **aminoalkanoic acid**) Any of a group of 24 **organic acids** that contain nitrogen, which are the building blocks of **proteins**. There are 20 amino acids in the human body: 12 non-essential (i.e. they can be synthesized in the body), alanine, aspartic acid, arginine, cysteine, **glutamic acid**, **glycine**, histidine, hydroxyproline, ornithine, proline, serine and tyrosine; 8 essential (i.e. they must be obtained from the diet), isoleucine, leucine, lysine, methionine, phenylalanine, threonine, tryptophan and valine. Amino acids are used to synthesize all the body proteins including enzymes and hormones.

aminoethanoic acid Alternative name for **glycine**.

ammonia solution Alternative name for **ammonium hydroxide**.

ammonium alginate (E403) An **emulsifier**, **stabilizer** and **thickener** made from **alginic acid**, which is in turn extracted from seaweed. It is also used as a **diluent** for some colouring agents. It is found in baked goods, cheese products, custard, ice cream and sweets.

ammonium bicarbonate Alternative name for **ammonium hydrogen carbonate**.

ammonium carbonate (503) An **alkali**, which may be used to neutralize acidity. As a mixture with **ammonium hydrogen carbonate**, it is employed as a **buffer**. In the presence of acids it generates carbon dioxide gas, and for this reason is also used as a **raising agent** in baking powders. It is found in baked goods, ice cream and sweets.

ammonium chloride (510; also called **sal ammoniac)** An inorganic **salt** employed as a source of nitrogen to feed yeast in brewing. It is also used as a **flavouring**, and can be found in bread and bread rolls. It should be avoided by anybody with a liver or kidney disorder, in whom it may affect the acidity of the urine.

ammonium ferric citrate (381; also called **ferric ammonium citrate)** A soluble iron compound, used medicinally as an iron supplement to treat iron-deficiency **anaemia** by stimulating the production of haemoglobin red blood cells. It is used in infant milk formulae and in flour for bread-making.

ammonium hydrogen carbonate (503; also called **ammonium bicarbonate)** An **alkali** salt employed, together with **ammonium carbonate**, as a **buffer**. In the presence of acids it generates carbon dioxide gas, and for this reason is used as an **aerating agent** and **raising agent**. It can be found in baked goods and ice cream.

ammonium hydroxide (527; also called **ammonia solution)** An **alkali** employed as a **solvent** and **diluent** for some food **colourings**. It is also found in some baked goods and foods made from cocoa.

ammonium phosphatides (442; also called ammonium salts of phosphatidic acid; emulsifier YN) An **emulsifier** and **stabilizer**, used in some foods containing chocolate or cocoa as an alternative to **lecithin**. It is not permitted in the US.

ammonium polyphosphates (545) Various ammonium salts of phosphoric acids employed as **emulsifiers** and **stabilizers**. The mixture is also used as a **sequestrant** to bind to (and thereby render harmless) traces of heavy metals. It is found in processed cheeses and meat products. Phosphorus is an important nutrient, and ammonium polyphosphates are used to feed yeasts in brewing.

anaemia A disorder in which there is a deficiency of red blood cells or of their oxygen-carrying pigment, haemoglobin. There are many possible causes, some inherited, but those most commonly connected with food include a deficiency in the diet of **iron** or of **vitamin B$_{12}$** (which leads to pernicious anaemia). Anaemia is a side-effect of alcoholism, because **alcoholic drinks** provide energy but few nutrients.

Foods rich in iron include meat (particularly liver), green leafy vegetables, and peas and beans. Iron is well absorbed by the body from animal foods, but although vegetable foods contain reasonable amounts it is less well absorbed. The presence of vitamin C improves the absorption of iron from vegetable foods. A normal balanced diet should contain sufficient iron, although supplements are sometimes prescribed for growing children and pregnant women.

Treatment of iron-deficiency anaemia is with iron tablets and, in very severe cases, blood transfusion. Vitamin B_{12} is a water-soluble vitamin present in animal foods, e.g. kidney, liver, eggs and dairy products, but absent in vegetable foods. It is fairly stable to heat, but is leached out into cooking water. Its deficiency is therefore a potential risk for strict vegetarians and vegans, who may require vitamin enriched foods or supplements. Certain food additives may also cause anaemia in people with **aspirin sensitivity** by interfering with haemoglobin in the blood.

anaphylaxis (also called **anaphylactic shock**) A severe and sudden allergic reaction, usually to a drug or animal venom (such as bee stings) but sometimes caused by a specific food in somebody who is abnormally sensitive to it (see **food allergy**). Symptoms are generalized and can be life-threatening; they include a rapid fall in blood pressure accompanied by an

asthma-like attack. The victim may vomit and lose control of bowel movements. Anaphylaxis requires emergency treatment, usually with injections of adrenaline and antihistamines. If the cause is a food, it must be stringently avoided for life.

angelica An aromatic umbelliferous plant whose leaves, seeds and stems are used as a flavouring. The candied stems are used for flavouring and decorating cakes and desserts.

angioedema (also called **angioneurotic oedema**) An allergic reaction that causes painless swelling of the face, usually of the eyes, lips and tongue; other parts of the body may also be affected. It may be a symptom of an allergic reaction to food or food additives, particularly some **azo dye** colouring agents. Angioedema resembles **urticaria** and may be accompanied by **asthma**-like symptoms. It is more common in people who have **aspirin sensitivity**. Treatment is with adrenaline, antihistamines and possibly other drugs. The food or food additive causing the reaction should be avoided.

angioneurotic oedema See **angioedema**.

aniline dye See **coal tar dye**.

anise An umbelliferous plant of the Mediterranean region whose aromatic seeds, which

17

taste like liquorice, are used as a flavouring in desserts and liqueurs, e.g. anisette, ouzo and Pernod.

aniseed A flavouring made from the seeds of **anise** and used particularly to flavour sweets.

anise pepper A spice from the Sichuan region of China, which has no taste when first bitten into, but later gives a strong, hot flavour.

annatto (E160b; also called bixin; norbixin; rocou) A widely used yellow to red **colouring** agent (a **carotenoid**), made from the pulpy outer part of the seeds of the annatto, a small tree that grows in tropical America, Africa and Asia. The dye may be extracted using water or vegetable oil, and is unaffected by cooking. It is also stable in salt water.

Annatto is used to give a yellow colour to many foods, including dairy products (butter and cheeses), margarine, creamed rice, cooking oil, breadcrumbs, crisps and smoked fish. Because it is of natural origin, it is favoured as an alternative to synthetic dyes in soft drinks and ice lollies.

anthocyanin (E163) A member of a group of similar red, blue or violet plant pigments used as **colouring** agents. They are found widely in red and purple fruits and flowers. Black grape

18

skins and red cabbage are used as commercial sources, from which anthocyanins are extracted using water or alcohol. The colour depends on acidity, being red in acids but bluer in alkaline conditions. **Sulphur dioxide** may be added as a preservative, and for this reason anthocyanins should be avoided by people with **asthma**. They are used to colour such foods as fruits, soups, soft drinks, sorbets and ice cream.

antibiotic A drug used for killing or preventing the growth of microorganisms, particularly bacteria. Antibiotics were themselves originally derived from moulds, but most are now produced synthetically. Long-term or unnecessary use may lead to the evolution of antibiotic-resistant strains of bacteria. Controversy in the food industry concerns the routine administration of antibiotics to young food animals and the possible retention of the drugs in meat for human consumption.

antibody A protein produced by the body in response to the presence of an **antigen** (such as an **allergen** or a disease-causing organism). Antibodies may remain in the bloodstream and confer immunity against further attacks by the antigen.

anti-browning agent A type of **antioxidant** added to cut fruits and fruit juices to prevent them from turning brown. **Ascorbic acid**, **citric acid** and **sulphur dioxide** are examples.

anti-caking agent A water-absorbing substance added to powdered foods to prevent the particles from sticking together so that they flow freely. Anti-caking agents include various salts (particularly phosphates), cellulose compounds and mineral powders. They are added to such foods as cocoa and custard powder, dried milk, icing sugar, instant soups and salt.

anti-foaming agent A substance added to a liquid food that is heated during manufacture to prevent it frothing when it boils or to reduce the risk of boiling over. Some anti-foaming agents also discourage the formation of scum, and are used in brewing and wine-making to limit the frothing produced during fermentation. Examples include **oxystearin** and the inert silicone known as **dimethylpolysiloxane**, which may be found in some jams, soups and syrups.

antigen A 'foreign' protein whose presence in the body stimulates the production of **antibodies**. Common antigens include bacteria, fungal spores, viruses and **allergens**, such as pollen and some food substances. See **food allergy**.

antioxidant A substance added to fats, oils and foods containing them to prevent them going rancid – that is, to stop them becoming oxidized on prolonged exposure to air. It additionally prevents the deterioration of fat-soluble vitamins in foods. Oxidation also causes discoloration of cut fruits (such as apples, which go brown), and antioxidants are added to the fruits to prevent this. Examples of antioxidants for fats, include gallates, **butylated hydroxyanisole** (BHA) and **butylated hydroxytoluene** (BHT), which are added to biscuits, soft drinks, margarine, cheese spread and the inner packaging of breakfast cereals. Common antioxidants used mainly with fruits are vitamins C and E and their numerous derivatives.

BHA and BHT are not permitted in foods for babies and young children, although they are allowed in foods such as crisps and nuts. Only the vitamins are permitted in baby foods. See also **anti-browning agent**.

Antioxidants in Food Regulations Regulations issued by the British Ministry of Agriculture, Fisheries and Food, which control the use of **antioxidants** in foods. The regulations list the substances that are permitted. Where appropriate, they specify the foods in which they may be used and the maximum levels that can be added. They also prohibit the sale of foods containing certain additives that are described as intended for babies or young children.

apple acid Alternative name for **malic acid**.

arrowroot An easily digested pure form of **starch** obtained from the rhizomes of a West Indian plant of the same name. It is used as a **thickener** in sauces, desserts and other cooked foods.

artificial In food labelling, a synonym for 'synthetic' or 'man-made', implying that the food or ingredient so described is not of **natural** origin. Even so, a pure substance produced in the laboratory (such as synthetic ascorbic acid, or vitamin C) may be chemically identical or nature identical to and therefore indistinguishable from the naturally occurring version. See also **artificial colour**; **artificial cream**; **artificial flavour**; **artificial sweetener**.

artificial colour There are many synthetic food **colouring** agents, of which 16 are allowed in the UK. Most are **coal tar dyes** or **azo dyes**, and some are both. Most also appear to be harmless, although two of them – **sunset yellow** and **tartrazine** – have been associated with **hyperactivity** in children and allergic reactions in susceptible people.

The following foods are not permitted to contain added colouring matter: any meat, game, poultry, fish, fruit or vegetable when in a raw or unprocessed state; bread, except for brown, malt and wholemeal bread; butter;

cocoa and chocolate products, except chocolate fillings and the coatings and decorations of filled chocolates; coffee and coffee products; cream; extra jam, extra jelly and chestnut purée; flour; fruit juices and fruit nectars; honey; milk, as specified in the Drinking Milk Regulations (1976), condensed or dried; mustard powder; sugar products, as specified by the Specified Sugar Products Regulations (1976), except those for use as ingredients in other foods; suet; tea, leaf or essence; table wines, as specified in the EC wine regulations.

Artificial colours may be introduced in more subtle ways by adding them not directly to food for human consumption, but to the feed of farm animals and fish to effect the colour of their eggs or flesh. Food labelling, e.g. on the skins of grapefruit and oranges or on the rind of bacon, may also introduce colour into food.

artificial cream A non-dairy cream substitute which is made from vegetable oils and water. Artificial creams may contain **stabilizers**, **emulsifiers**, **acidity regulators**, **flavourings** and **colourings**. Some claim to be lower in fat and calories than standard cream.

artificial flavour A synthetic substance added to impart a particular flavour to food, such as the smoky taste of some smoked cheese, fish or meat. Nearly all artificial flavours are exact

23

chemical copies of the natural version, and indeed only four of the flavourings permitted in Britain are entirely synthetic with no exact natural counterpart. See also **flavour enhancer**.

artificial sweetener   A synthetic substance added to foods to impart a sweet taste (as opposed to a natural sugar derived from plants or honey). Many are very much sweeter than sugar and are consequently used in very small quantities. They include **mannitol** and **sorbitol** (which occur naturally but are synthesized for commercial use), **acesulfame-K** and **aspartame** (with some restrictions on permitted use), **thaumatin** and **saccharin** and its salts; **sodium cyclamate** is also extensively used outside the UK.

Most artificial sweeteners have little or no energy content (and are often termed low-calorie sweetener), and are useful for people who wish to reduce sugar intake while retaining a sweet taste to their food. They are also used by diabetics who must control their sugar intake. The **Sweeteners in Food Regulations** do not permit the use of sweeteners in foods prepared specifically for babies and young children, unless the foods are intended for those with special dietary requirements.

ascorbic acid (E300; also called **L-ascorbic acid**; **vitamin C**)   A vitamin that occurs naturally in fresh fruits and vegetables and which can also be synthesized or genetically engineered. In addition to its use as a vitamin (for instance it is added to dehydrated potatoes to replace the vitamin C lost in processing), ascorbic acid is employed as an **anti-browning agent** and **anti-oxidant**, particularly in brewing lager. It is also used as a **preservative**, to retain the colour of meat, and as an **improving agent** for flour. Ascorbic acid is found in breakfast foods, baked products, most fruit products, canned meats and baby foods.

ascorbyl palmitate Alternative name for **6–0-palmitoyl-L-ascorbic acid**.

aspartame An **artificial sweetener** that is about 200 times as sweet as sugar. It is commonly used in low-calorie or 'diet' soft drinks and yoghurts because it has no calorific value and as a table-top sweetener in capsule, powder and liquid form. It is the most commercially successful artificial sweetener and is used in Nutrasweet and Canderel. It tends to lose its sweetness on prolonged heating and is not suitable for cooking. Aspartame contains phenylanlanine, and should be avoided by people suffering from the inherited disorder phenylketonuria (PKN), who cannot metabolize this substance. It is permitted in the UK but not in seven other European countries.

Although controversy continues over aspartame, it is considered safe by the Ministry of Agriculture, Fisheries and Food and remains on their list of permitted sweeteners.

aspic A savoury jelly made from the liquor in which fish or meat has been cooked, used in canned meats and meat pies. It is often replaced by cheaper seaweed extracts, e.g. **agar** and **carrageenan**. It is also used for glazing savoury dishes in the home.

aspirin sensitivity In some people aspirin produces asthma-like symptoms, which are probably an allergic reaction to the drug. About 20% of such people are also sensitive to certain food additives, particularly **azo dye** colouring agents, glutamate **flavour enhancers**, benzoate **preservatives** and gallate **antioxidants**. See **anaemia**.

asthma A lung disorder in which the bronchial tubes narrow and go into spasm, causing difficult breathing and shortness of breath, often with coughing. It may be present from childhood or associated with stress. A common cause is an allergy, frequently a **food allergy**, although it is often unclear whether the cause is the ingestion of food or the inhalation of odours. Similar symptoms may also be caused by **aspirin sensitivity**. Like people with aspirin sensitivity, asthmatics should avoid certain food additives, such as **azo dyes, benzoates, gallates** and **glutamates**. The common preservative **sulphur dioxide** (and sulphites) may also trigger an asthma attack, and should be avoided if possible – although its presence is not revealed in **alcoholic drinks**, for example.

autolysed yeast   A form of yeast in which the individual cells have been ruptured. This helps to release the various B complex vitamins they contain. It is a process frequently used in the production of **yeast extract**.

aversion   See **food aversion**.

azodicarbonamide (927; also called **azoformamide; azo dicarboxylic acid; azo bisformamide**)   An **improving agent** or maturing agent for flour used in making bread, which enables the dough to be usable even if fermentation conditions vary widely. It is seldom used in the UK.

azo dye   A member of a large group of synthetic chemicals, widely used as **colours** in foods. Many are also **coal tar** dyes. Their molecules have a pair of nitrogen atoms – the colour-producing azo group – to which some people are sensitive, including people with **aspirin sensitivity, asthma** and other allergies such as **eczema**. Azo dyes have also been associated

27

with **hyperactivity** in children. In sensitive people they may cause a wide variety of symptoms, including blurred vision, asthma-like attacks, **angioedema**, **urticaria**, and running nose and eyes. There are currently ten azo dyes with E numbers: **amaranth**; **black PN**; **brown FK**; **carmoisine**; **brown HT**; **pigment rubine**; **ponceau 4R**; **red 2G**; **sunset yellow FCF** and **tartrazine**.

azoformamide Alternative name for **azodicarbonamide**.

azorubine Alternative name for **carmoisine**.

baby food There are various regulations that control the composition and production of foods for babies. In particular, certain additives that are permitted in foods for adult consumption are not permitted in baby foods. They include certain **acidity regulators** (e.g. malic acid), most **antioxidants**, and all **colourings** (except the vitamins riboflavin and beta-carotene), **artificial sweeteners** (e.g. mannitol, sorbitol), **flavour enhancers** (e.g. glutamic acid and its compounds, sodium inosinate) and **preservatives** (particularly sodium nitrate).

baked beans A popular vegetable made from haricot beans, tomatoes, sugar, salt, starch, vinegar and spices. Baked beans are a good source of protein and fibre, have a low fat content and are usually free from additives. Low or no-added sugar varieties are also available.

baking powder A **raising agent** usually consisting of a mixture of an acid, e.g. **potassium tartrate** (cream of tartar), and an alkali, e.g. **bicarbonate of soda**, mixed with a starch or flour base. In a moist mixture these react together to generate carbon dioxide gas causing the food, such as cakes and bread, to rise during cooking. Double-action baking powder contains two acids, one which reacts at room temperature and one which reacts at the cooking temperature.

baking soda An alternative name for **sodium hydrogen carbonate** (sodium bicarbonate).

balm An imprecise term for various aromatic oils and resins obtained from tropical trees, used for healing and soothing purposes.

barley water A soft drink made from fruit juice, citrus juice, sugar and barley flour. Undiluted barley water must contain at least 15% fruit juice and ready-to-drink versions at least 3%. **Stabilizers**, **preservatives** and **flavourings** may be added and some varieties are sweetened with **artificial sweeteners**.

base A substance that neutralizes an **acid**; a base that dissolves in water is an **alkali**. In the food industry, bases are used to reduce acidity or increase alkalinity. They are also employed as **aerating agents** or **raising agents** (or as components of them). Most common bases in foods are carbonates, hydrogen carbonates (bicarbonates), hydroxides or oxides.

basil (also called **sweet basil**) An aromatic herb made from the leaves of a labiate plant that grows in Asia and Europe. So-called wild basil comes from a different but related European species. Dried basil is used to flavour braised or stewed beef, particularly those containing tomatoes, and fresh basil is used in salads.

bay An aromatic herb made from the leaves of a Mediterranean laurel shrub. The dried leaves are used for flavouring savoury foods, particularly soups, stocks and stews.

beer An **alcoholic drink** made by fermenting a watery mixture of hops and malt – sometimes with added sugar – using yeast. Strictly, beer should be distinguished from ale, which uses no hops and has the yeast at the top of the mash (not the bottom), and lager, which is an extra-light beer that is traditionally kept for six months before being sold. Most references to beer and brewing in this book include all these types, unless they are specifically identified.

Various additives are used in beers that are brewed commercially in large quantities, from **caramel** for colour to **foam stabilizers** to give a persistent head and **sulphur dioxide** (or sulphites) as a **preservative**. Some countries, notably Germany, ban the use of additives in beers for home consumption. As with other alcoholic drinks, beer with an alcoholic strength by volume of more than 1.2% does not have to give an ingredient list on the label or can.

beeswax (901) A type of wax obtained from honeycombs, described as yellow beeswax in its natural state or white beeswax if it has been bleached. It is employed to impart a glaze or polish to foods (particularly biscuits, cakes and confectionery) and as a component of various fruit and honey flavourings for ice cream and soft drinks. It is also used as a **release agent** in food manufacture. Beeswax contains resins that may produce an allergic reaction in people who are sensitive to them.

beetroot red (E162; also called **betanin**; **betanidin)** A deep purple-red natural **colouring** agent obtained from beetroot, which has limited use in cooked foods because it is broken down by heat. It is also sensitive to acidity, becoming purple in alkaline conditions. Beetroot red is used in ice lollies, fruit products (including yoghurts, jellies and other desserts) and in tomato and oxtail soups. **Sodium nitrate** or **benzoic acid** may be added as a preservative, and so foods containing it should not be fed to babies or to children with a history of **hyperactivity**.

behavioural problems Aberrations in behaviour have been associated with certain food additives, such as **antioxidants**, **artificial colours** and **flavourings**. Although a series of exhaustive tests on schoolchildren and prison inmates in the US have been carried out the results are still not conclusive. It has not been established whether the actual cause is the additives or a generally poor diet. A diet rich in sugar was also found to be a cause of behavioural problems. See also **hyperactivity**.

bentonite (558; also called **bentonitum; soap clay)** A type of clay of volcanic origin similar to fuller's earth, found in the western US. It is employed as an **anti-caking agent** (because it absorbs water), **emulsifier** and for clarifying beer and wine (in which it may be found). It is also used to aid the filtration of yeast residues from beer.

benzoate of soda Alternative name for **sodium benzoate**.

32

benzoic acid (E210) A **preservative** that occurs in various fruits but is produced synthetically for the food industry. It works only in an acidic environment, in which it is effective against bacteria and some fungi (moulds). It may be used to preserve a food, or another food additive. Benzoic acid turns up in a wide variety of foods, particularly in jams, pickles, syrups, soft drinks and other foods based on fruit. Benzoic acid has been associated with **hyperactivity** in children and sensitivity reactions in people with **aspirin sensitivity**, **asthma** or **urticaria**. Asthmatics should particularly avoid benzoic acid if it is used in combination with **sodium hydrogen sulphite** (sodium bisulphite). Foods that are permitted to contain benzoic acid may also have **sodium benzoate**, **potassium benzoate** and **calcium benzoate** added to them.

bergamot 1. Also called **bergamot orange**: an Asian citrus tree whose fruits yield a fragrant oil, used as a flavouring. 2. A lemon-scented Mediterranean herb related to the mint family. Its flowers may be crystallized and its fresh leaves used in salads or to make herb tea.

best before date A date, required on the labels of pre-packed foods (except frozen foods), which states the day, month and year by which the food should be sold and consumed;

storage conditions should also be stated. For foods whose shelf life is between 6 weeks and 3 months, the best before day and month need only be stated (along with the storage conditions). For foods with a shelf life of between 3 and 19 months, only the month and year need be given. Foods with a shelf life of more than 18 months do not require a best before date. See also **sell by date**; **use by date**; APPENDIX I, ADDITIVE-FREE SHOPPING.

beta-apo—8′-carotenal (E160e; also called **beta-apo-caretenal; beta—8′-apocarotenal**) A **carotenoid** pigment that occurs in the flesh and skin of citrus fruits, although only synthetic pigments are employed by the food industry. It is used to impart an orange colour to such foods as cheese slices and soups.

beta-carotene (E160a) An orange-yellow **colouring** agent that occurs naturally in carrots, oranges and tomatoes but is mainly made synthetically. Its properties and uses are the same as those of **alpha-carotene**.

betanin Alternative name for **beetroot red**.

BHA Abbreviation of **butylated hydroxyanisole**.

BHT Abbreviation of **butylated hydroxytoluene**.

bicarbonate of soda Alternative name of **sodium hydrogen carbonate**.

biphenyl (E230; also called **diphenyl; phenyl benzene)** A **preservative** that acts specifically on the fungi that make citrus fruits go mouldy. It is applied to the unpeeled fruits or to paper for wrapping them. Biphenyl can diffuse through the peel and turn up in foods made from the fruit (such as marmalade). For this reason, citrus fruits should be peeled before use, although a small piece of orange or lemon rind presents a negligible hazard.

biscuit A small flat baked cake made from dough. There are many varieties of biscuit, both sweet and savoury. Sweet biscuits have a high sugar content. Many types of additives are used in the manufacture of biscuits, including **antioxidants**, **colourings**, **emulsifiers**, **flavourings**, **preservatives**, **stabilizers** and **sweeteners**, although some brands are free from additives.

bixin Alternative name for **annatto**.

black peppercorn The dried unripe berries of the pepper plant, which is a native of the East Indies. Commercial ground black pepper is a pungent condiment made by grinding the peppercorns and their husks.

black PN (E151; also called **brilliant black PN**; **food black)** A synthetic **colouring** agent, both an **azo dye** and a **coal tar dye**, employed to colour foods black. It is used in some blackcurrant fillings, chocolate desserts and brown sauce. Other azo dyes have been associated with **hyperactivity** in children, and black PN is banned in several countries, including Canada and the US, but not in the UK.

blanch A method of pre-cooking food by plunging a fruit or vegetable into boiling water for a short time. Blanching is often used before quick-freezing.

bleaching agent A substance employed to make flour whiter, particularly flour for bread-making, and as such is also a member of the larger category of **flour treatment agents**. The principal bleaches used for this purpose are benzoyl peroxide, **chlorine** and **chlorine dioxide**. The latter two are also bactericidal, but they destroy some of the nutrients and vitamins in flour.

borage A plant native to the Mediterranean region whose young leaves have the flavour of cucumber. The young leaves can be added to salads, but it is mainly used in drinks such as Pimms. The herb can also be used as a tea infusion.

Bordeaux mustard A French mustard made by blending in unfermented Bordeaux wine. It is dark brown and has a strong acid aromatic taste. Bordeaux mustard is a very popular accompaniment to steak.

bottled water Still or sparkling water sold in bottles as an alternative to drinking tap water. Bottled water can come from wells, natural springs or from reprocessed tap water. Sparkling water may be naturally or artificially carbonated. Some bottled waters contain considerable amounts of minerals, again either present naturally or added during the bottling process.

All bottled waters are controlled by laws. Some are controlled only by public water supply laws, but natural mineral water is controlled by an EC directive which prevents any therapeutic claims being made. Bottled water is available in glass and plastic bottles, although glass bottles provide more protection against bacterial contamination than plastic.

botulism A very serious form of food poisoning. It is caused by eating canned or bottled food contaminated with *Clostridium botulinum* bacteria, which can survive and multiply in anaerobic (oxygen-free) conditions. The symptoms result from the action of the poison botulin, which is a powerful neurotoxin produced by the bacteria. It affects the central nervous system and in severe cases causes respiratory paralysis and death.

bouquet garni A mixture of herbs, usually in small individual bunches or sachets, used for flavouring savoury dishes, e.g. stews, casseroles, soups and stocks. A simple bouquet garni can be made by tying together fresh or dried parsley, thyme, bay, clove and peppercorn in a small piece of muslin.

bowel problems Intestinal disorders have been associated with some food additives in susceptible people. Flatulence can be caused by very large intakes of fibrous substances such as **agar**, **alginates**, and cellulose and its compounds, which may also inhibit the absorption of certain nutrients. Even natural **bran** can cause problems if eaten in excess.

Mineral hydrocarbons such as liquid paraffin are known to have a laxative effect. They may also prevent the absorption in the intestine of fats and fat-soluble vitamins. They are used in food processing as **glazing agents** and coatings (particularly on fruits and confectionery), as well as for lubricating machinery.

bran Fibrous material consisting of the outer husks of grain. It contains an acid (phytic acid) which in large amounts inhibits the absorption of calcium and some trace elements in the intestine. Bran is a commonly recommended dietary fibre, although too much can cause problems such as constipation (which the bran is probably taken to prevent in the first place). It is often added to foods, particularly bread and breakfast cereals, to increase their dietary fibre content.

bran bread A type of bread in which the flour has been enriched with added bran. Any variety of flour may be used and the bread may also contain any of the additives permitted in standard **bread**.

bread Various substances may be added to mass-produced bread, both to the flour (such as a **bleaching agent**, **flour treatment agent** or **improving agent**) and the dough (such as **caramel** to give colour to brown bread). Another common additive, particularly in white bread, is an agent to kill the mould that forms **rope**. If the bread is pre-packed or wrapped, the ingredients must be listed on the wrapper. Unwrapped bread, in common with many other foods sold in 'loose' form, is not required to provide an ingredient list. See also **brown bread**; **flour**; **white bread**; **wholemeal bread**.

Bread and Flour Regulations A set of regulations issued by the Ministry of Agriculture, Fisheries and Food that controls the use of additives in all types of **bread**.

breadcrumbs   The crumbs of bread that have been dried to reduce the water content and which are used for coating food prior to cooking. Commercially prepared breadcrumbs are often bright orange in colour because of the use of **colouring**, particularly **tartrazine**. Some brands are available that do not contain additives and which are made with wholemeal bread.

breakfast cereal   Any of a number of ready-to-eat products made from cereals which are eaten predominantly at breakfast time, usually with milk and often with added sugar. Corn, wheat and rice are the most common cereals used. Wholegrain cereals have high fibre contents and cereals generally have low fat contents, although the amount of added sugar and salt may be quite high. Many manufacturers add iron and vitamins to enrich their products, but in general other types of additives are not used.

breathing problems   The most common disorders of breathing caused by foods are the **asthma**-like symptoms in a person suffering from a **food allergy**. People who already have asthma or suffer from **aspirin sensitivity** are advised to avoid certain food additives, such as **azo dyes** and some **flavour enhancers** and **preservatives**.

brilliant black PN   Alternative name for **black PN**.

brilliant blue FCF (133)   A synthetic blue **coal tar dye** used as a **colouring** agent, sometimes combined with **tartrazine**, a yellow **azo dye**, to create a green colour. It is used in jellies and to dye canned processed peas, but has been banned in 11 European countries although not in the UK. It is recommended that children with a history of **hyperactivity** should avoid this additive.

brown bread   A bread made from flour which has had about 15% of the bran and germ removed during milling. According to the **Bread and Flour Regulations**, the fibre content of brown bread must not be less than 0.6%. Brown bread is permitted to contain most of the additives found in **white bread** as well as those permitted in **wholemeal bread**.

brown FK (154; also called **food brown**; **kipper brown**)   A mixture of six **azo dyes** with **sodium chloride** or **sodium sulphate**, employed as a **colouring** agent. It is the only brown dye that tolerates salt solution (brine). For this reason brown FK is used to dye kippers and mackerel before smoking and to give a brown colour to 'barbecued' chicken and ham.

Two of its component dyes have produced

toxic effects in experimental animals, and because it contains azo dyes it should be avoided by people with **asthma** or **aspirin sensitivity** and children with a history of **hyperactivity**. Brown FK is already banned in many countries, including the US and the whole of the EC with the exception of the UK and Ireland.

brown HT (155; also called **chocolate brown HT**) A synthetic **azo dye** and **coal tar dye**, used to give a brown colour to pickles, soft drinks and chocolate-flavoured products that contain no cocoa. It should be avoided by people with **asthma** or **aspirin sensitivity** and children with a history of **hyperactivity**. Brown FT is banned in Australia, the US and eight European countries, but not in the UK.

brown soya oil See **oxidatively polymerized soya bean oil**.

buffer A substance that holds the **acid–alkali** balance of a solution at a particular level despite the addition of extra acid or alkali. Most buffers are sodium or potassium **salts** of weak acids such as acetic, carbonic, citric or lactic acid. Acid salts, such as **hydrogen carbonates** (bicarbonates) and **hydrogen phosphates**, are also used as buffers. Many are counted as

acidity regulators. They are commonly used in canned fruits, jams, jellies, soups and sweets.

bulking agent   A substance that adds to the bulk of a food without adding to its calorific value, usually because it cannot be digested by humans, but passes, virtually unaltered, through the digestive system. For this reason bulking agents are common in slimming foods. Most consist of cellulose or one of its compounds. Certain gums are also used as bulking agents, although these usually do make a contribution to calorie intake. Sometimes they are used to bulk out more expensive substances.

burnet (also called **salad burnet**)   A plant of the rose family whose leaves are used in salads.

butter   A smooth, fatty, whitish-yellow paste made by churning cream. Ordinary butter consists of 85% fat and 15% water, and contains vitamins A, D and E. The only additive commonly used during manufacture is **salt**, which enhances flavour and inhibits the growth of bacteria and moulds, although unsalted butter is readily available. **Acidity regulators** may also be employed to ensure that the pasteurized cream, used to make butter, is of the correct acidity.

The colour of butter is due to **carotene**, which comes from the cows' diet. Sweet butter is made from fresh cream and lactic butter is made from cream that is cultured with **lactic acid**; this produces bacteria which cause the souring. See also **margarine**.

buttermilk The watery liquid that separates from the fat when cream is churned to make **butter**. It consists of water, protein, **lactose** and minerals. Buttermilk is used as an ingredient in various dairy foods. Cultured buttermilk is made by adding a culture to skimmed milk.

butylated hydroxyanisole (E320; also called **BHA)** A synthetic **antioxidant** commonly added to vegetable oils, fats and foods containing them (e.g. chips and crisps) to prevent them going rancid; a process that is caused by oxidation of the fat by oxygen in the air and is accelerated by sunlight. It may be used with a **synergist**, e.g. **citric** or **tartaric acid**, to enhance its action, and sometimes another antioxidant, e.g. **butylated hydroxytoluene** (BHT) or a **gallate**, is also included.

Butylated hydroxyanisole causes an allergic reaction in some people who are sensitive to it. It is used in a large range of foods, from cheese spread and pastry to biscuits, crisps and various packaged convenience foods. It is also added to margarine, cooking fat and vegetable oil. BHA is not normally allowed in foods intended specifically for babies or young children, and it is recommended that it should be avoided by children with a history of **hyperactivity**. It is banned in Japan.

butylated hydroxytoluene (E321; also called **BHT)** A widely used synthetic **antioxidant** commonly added to vegetable oils, fats and foods containing them to prevent them going rancid (a process that is caused by oxidation of the fat by oxygen in the air and is accelerated by sunlight). It may be used with a **synergist**, such as **citric** or **tartaric acid**, to enhance its action, and sometimes another antioxidant, e.g. **butylated hydroxyanisole** (BHA) or a gallate, is also included.

Butylated hydroxytoluene causes an allergic rash in some people who are sensitive to it. It is used in a large range of foods, particularly snacks and various packaged convenience foods. It is also added to margarine, cooking fat and vegetable oil, but, although it is cheaper than BHA, it is less tolerant of high temperatures. BHT is not allowed in foods intended specifically for babies or young children, and it is recommended that it should be avoided by children with a history of **hyperactivity**.

caffeine A mildly stimulant and **diuretic** alkaloid drug that occurs in various plants, including coffee, cocoa, cola and tea. It is also manufactured synthetically for medicinal use.

Caffeine is one of the substances that can trigger a **migraine** attack in susceptible people. **Decaffeinated** beverages are now available.

cake A mix of fat, sugar, eggs and flour, often enriched with dried fruit or flavoured with chocolate, spices or fruit juice and baked in a variety of shapes. Commercially baked cakes tend to have high fat and sugar and low fibre contents. They may also contain additives including **antioxidants**, **colouring**, **emulsifiers**, **flavourings** and **preservatives**. Wholemeal cakes with higher fibre contents are becoming more available, but home-baking is the best way to guarantee low-fat, low-sugar, high-fibre cakes containing the minimum of food additives.

cake mix A ready-to-use mixture of dry ingredients requiring the addition of liquid in the form of water or milk and possibly egg, before baking. Cake mixes tend to contain a variety of additives including **antioxidants**, **colours**, **emulsifiers**, **flavourings** and **preservatives**.

calciferol Alternative name for **vitamin D**.

calcium A metallic element that is an essential part of the diet for the maintenance of healthy bones and teeth. It is especially important for growing children, pregnant women and lactating mothers, and a deficiency of calcium causes rickets in children and osteomalacia in adults. Osteoporosis involves an excessive loss of calcium from the bones in old age, leaving them brittle and prone to fracture. Although increasing calcium intake when an adult is unlikely to effect the disease, ensuring an adequate intake in childhood appears to have a preventative effect.

The proper absorption of calcium from the diet depends on the action of **vitamin D**, and is inhibited by phytic acid, a substance present in wholegrain cereals, nuts and pulses (see **bowel problems**). Foods rich in calcium include dairy products (particularly cheese), fish, beans and green leafy vegetables. It is a component of a great number of food additives – only potassium and sodium occur more frequently.

calcium acetate (E263; also called **calcium ethanoate)** The calcium salt of **acetic** (ethanoic) **acid**, used as a **buffer** and **acidity regulator** (to control the acidity of jellies and fruit fillings), **sequestrant** and **stabilizer**. It is also used in bread-making to kill the spores of moulds that can form **rope**.

calcium alginate (E404) A **gelling agent** made from **alginic acid**, in turn extracted from seaweeds, also employed as an **emulsifier, stabilizer** and **thickener** – for example, it is added to jam to prevent it being too runny in baked

47

cakes and tarts. It is also found in cheese products, ice cream and instant desserts. Overconsumption of alginate, as with other fibres, can affect the absorption of certain minerals in the intestines.

calcium aluminium silicate Alternative name for **aluminium calcium silicate**.

calcium L-ascorbate (E302; also called **calcium ascorbate)** The calcium salt of **ascorbic acid** (vitamin C), employed to add the vitamin to foods. It is also used as an **antioxidant** and to preserve the colour of meat. It is found in some clear soups, milk products and stock cubes.

calcium benzoate (E213; also called **monocalcium benzoate)** A **preservative**, the calcium salt of **benzoic acid**, used to destroy or prevent the growth of bacteria and fungi in concentrated fruit juice. It is also found in bottled sauces and soft drinks. Foods containing it should be avoided by people who suffer from **asthma**, **aspirin sensitivity**, or any other type of allergy, and by children with a history of **hyperactivity**.

calcium bisulphite Alternative name for **calcium hydrogen sulphite**.

calcium carbonate (E170; also called **chalk)** A **base**, occasionally employed to reduce the acidity of wine, and a source of **calcium**, added to flour for making white bread and other baked products. It is used as a **releasing agent** in the manufacture of vitamin pills, as a **firming agent** for canned fruit and vegetables, and as an **anti-caking agent** in various powdered foods. Calcium carbonate may also be used to give a white surface colour to sweets.

calcium chloride (509) A **firming agent** employed to retain the crispness of some canned and pickled vegetables. It is also used as a **sequestrant**. It may be found in dried or condensed milk and in cheese products. The malt used in brewing may have added calcium chloride, to even out natural variations in the calcium content of the local water supply.

calcium citrate (E333) **Citric acid** has three replaceable hydrogen atoms and can form three different calcium salts, termed monocalcium citrate, dicalcium citrate and tricalcium citrate, all of which are given the designation E333. They are employed as **buffers** to control the acidity of jams, jellies, sweets and wines, as **firming agents** (e.g. in canned tomatoes), as **emulsifiers** (e.g. in milk products and processed cheeses) and as **sequestrants**. These citrates are also used to add a lemon flavour to soft drinks and sweets.

calcium dihydrogen di-L-glutamate (623; also called **calcium glutamate)** A **flavour enhancer**, also employed as a substitute for **salt** in 'diet' foods. It is used mainly in clear soups and dried convenience foods, and is not recommended for very young babies (under 3 months).

calcium disodium EDTA Alternative name for **calcium disodium ethylenediamine tetraacetate**.

calcium disodium ethylenediamine tetraacetate (385; also called **calcium disodium EDTA)** A **sequestrant** that 'mops up' traces of heavy metals such as copper, iron, manganese, nickel, aluminium and zinc. The metals, present in manufactured foods that have come into contact with machinery, can affect foods in various ways, particularly with regard to colour and flavour. It is effective only in water-based foods, such as canned fish, mushrooms and shellfish. Too much of the additive could sequester metallic trace elements that are necessary in the body for normal good health. It is also used as a **synergist** for **antioxidants**, and may be found in mayonnaise and salad dressings.

calcium ethanoate Alternative name for **calcium acetate**.

calcium formate (E238; also called **calcium methanoate)** The calcium salt of **formic acid**, once employed as a **preservative**. It is a **diuretic** and can affect the balance of salts in the body, particularly of potassium. Its use is not permitted in the UK and the US.

calcium gluconate (578) A versatile synthetic food additive employed as a **buffer**, **firming agent** and **sequestrant**. It can be found in canned fruit and vegetables. It is used medically as a calcium supplement and to treat **urticaria** and other allergic conditions.

calcium glutamate Alternative name for **calcium dihydrogen di-L-glutamate**.

calcium hydrogen malate (352) An acid salt of **malic acid**, used as a **buffer** and **firming agent** in some jams and canned fruits.

calcium hydrogen orthophosphate (E341b; also called **calcium hydrogen phosphate; calcium phosphate dibasic; dicalcium phosphate**, or **DCP; secondary calcium phosphate) Orthophosphoric acid** has three replaceable hydrogen atoms, and in this acid salt two of them have been replaced by a calcium atom, while the third hydrogen remains. This accounts in part for the large number of names (as with other salts of phosphoric acid).

It also has a large number of uses. The presence of phosphorus makes it a mineral nutrient, added to cereals, animal feeds and foods for yeast (in brewing and wine-making). It is also employed as an **emulsifier**, **firming agent** and as a **synergist** with **antioxidants**. Its slightly abrasive properties account for its use in some toothpastes. Foods that contain it include snacks based on potato; baked products; cream, ice cream and milk powders; canned cherries for filling fruit pies.

calcium hydrogen phosphate Alternative name for **dicalcium diphosphate**.

calcium hydrogen sulphite (E227; also called calcium bisulphite) A **preservative** commonly used in jams and jellies, and to stop fermentation (by killing the yeast) in brewing and wine-making. It is also used to wash out wine barrels and beer casks, and may consequently be found in these drinks. It is also employed as a **firming agent** to retain the crispness of canned fruit and vegetables. However, it decomposes some of the thiamin (vitamin B_1) in such foods. In the presence of acids – even the weak acids found in foods – calcium hydrogen sulphite generates **sulphur dioxide** gas, and so it should be strictly avoided by people with **asthma**. It may also cause stomach upsets and allergic reactions in the skin, and is not recommended for children with a history of **hyperactivity**.

calcium hydroxide (526; also called **slaked lime)** An **alkali** employed to neutralize acids in foods, e.g. barley (used to make malt for brewing); it may also be added to the malt to control its calcium content if this varies in the local water supply. Calcium hydroxide is employed as a **firming agent**, and may be found in snacks made from potato flour, cocoa products, fruit products and cheese.

calcium lactate (E327) The calcium salt of **lactic acid**. It is employed as an **antioxidant** and **synergist** for other antioxidants in cheeses and low-fat spreads, as well as a **firming agent** and to prevent the discoloration of canned fruits and vegetables. It is also used in the making of jams and jellies because of its property as a **buffer** and **acidity regulator**. Calcium lactate may also be used as a yeast nutrient and in medicine to treat calcium deficiency.

calcium malate (352) A calcium salt of **malic acid**, employed as a **buffer** in jams and jellies and as a **firming agent** in canned fruits. It is also used to imitate the flavour of apples.

calcium methanoate Alternative name for **calcium formate**.

calcium oxide (529; also called **lime; quicklime)** A **base**, employed as a **processing aid,**

for example in bread-making and in products containing cocoa.

calcium phosphate tribasic Alternative name for **tricalcium diorthophosphate**.

calcium phytate A calcium salt of phytic acid, which occurs naturally in **bran** and foods (such as bread) containing it. In the intestines phytic acid from such sources may combine with **calcium** and thereby reduce its absorption into the body. Calcium phytate is used as a **sequestrant** in baked goods, soft drinks and processed vegetables.

calcium polyphosphates (544) Calcium salts of polyphosphoric acid, employed as an **emulsifier** in processed cheeses and as a **firming agent** and **sequestrant**. It is also used as a supplementary source of the minerals calcium and phosphorus (e.g. in instant desserts based on milk). It is not used in the UK food industry.

calcium propanoate Alternative name for **calcium propionate**.

calcium propionate (E282; also called calcium propanoate) An organic calcium salt that occurs naturally in fermented foods, but is synthesized for use in the food industry. It is employed as a **preservative** and mould inhibitor, particularly to kill the spores of moulds that produce **rope**. It has been known to cause rashes in bakery workers and there is a possible link with **migraine** attacks. Calcium propionate may be found in frozen pizzas, processed cheese and various kinds of bread and baked goods.

calcium saccharin   See **saccharin**.

calcium salts of fatty acids (E470)   Chemically these substances are soaps, employed in the food industry as **anti-caking agents**, **emulsifiers** and **stabilizers**. They may be found in some crisps and other crispy snacks, icing sugar, and in cake and soup mixes.

calcium silicate (552)   A mineral substance whose anhydrous form absorbs moisture and is for this reason employed as an **anti-caking agent** in powdered foods such as icing sugar, salt and flavoured salts and in the powdered drinks in vending machines. It is also used as a **glazing agent** on meat pies, as a **release agent** in making sweets, and as a surface **coating agent** to prevent stickiness on chewing gum and to keep grains of rice separate.

calcium sorbate (E203)   A synthesized calcium salt of **sorbic acid** (for which it may be used as an alternative), employed as a **preserva-**

tive for destroying or limiting the growth of bacteria and fungi. Typical foods that contain it include baked goods, pie fillings, and various fermented milk products, such as yoghurt.

calcium stearoyl-2-lactylate (E482) A synthetic **emulsifier** and **stabilizer** made from **lactic acid** and used in some bread, powdered gravy and artificial cream (so that it can be whipped). It is banned in the US.

calcium sulphate (516; also called **gypsum**; **plaster of Paris)** A common, naturally occurring mineral employed as a **firming agent**, yeast nutrient and as a supplementary source of **calcium**. It may also be added to maintain the calcium content of the local water supply used in the malting process at breweries. It can be found in flour, baked products and cheese products.

calcium sulphite (E226) A **preservative** and **firming agent** which is used as an alternative to **calcium hydrogen sulphite**, particularly in making cider. It may also be found in various fruit juices. In the presence of acids it generates **sulphur dioxide** and so it should be avoided by people with **asthma**. Calcium sulphite may also cause stomach upsets and allergic reactions in the skin, and is not recommended for children with a history of **hyperactivity**.

calcium tetrahydrogen diorthophosphate (E341a; also called acid calcium phosphate, or ACP; monobasic; monobasic calcium phosphate, or MCP; monocalcium orthophosphate) A synthesized version of the mineral that occurs naturally as apatite – for a note on the naming of such compounds, see **calcium hydrogen orthophosphate**. It is an acid salt, employed as a **buffer** and as an **acid** ingredient in baking powders and self-raising flours (where it acts as a **raising agent**), and products containing them, such as cake mixes and pastry mixes. It is also used as an **improving agent** in flour for bread and other baked foods that are made with yeast. It is a **firming agent** (e.g. for canned tomatoes) and **sequestrant**. It is also used in instant milk-based drinks and desserts.

camomile (also called **chamomile**) A Eurasian composite plant whose leaves are used as a herb and to make a form of tea.

cancer A blanket term for various disorders, many of which are characterized by the presence of a malignant tumour that results from the runaway replication of tissue cells. Untreated, the tumour may spread to invade other parts of the body. Leukaemia, in which there is an excess of misshapen white blood cells, is also regarded as a form of cancer.

Substances that cause cancer are termed carcinogens. A few have been found in certain foods and food additives, even if they are known to cause cancer only in massive doses to experimental animals. In fact, one of the main reasons for the extensive testing of foods and food additives – and the continued use of experimental animals to do so – is to detect potential carcinogens. It may even be that a combination of certain food factors makes the development of cancer more likely, even if individually none of these factors is carcinogenic.

The method of cooking the food may also be significant; barbecuing, grilling and roasting are less favoured than other ways of preparing meat, for example. The farming practice of using hormones to increase fat-production by meat animals (now banned in many countries) has also been linked to the incidence of cancer in people who eat the meat.

There is a long list of carcinogenic chemicals – or potentially carcinogenic ones – that have been associated with foods and food additives, mostly based on the results of experiments with animals. They may be components of foods, or they may be chemicals that are produced on storage, cooking or even in the body after the foods been eaten. They include some **antioxidants** (e.g. **BHT**), **colours** (e.g. **amaranth**, **carbon black**) and **preservatives** (e.g. **sodium nitrate** and **sodium nitrite**).

canned fish Any of a variety of fish that has

been canned to preserve it and increase the shelf-life of an otherwise highly nutritious but perishable food. The most common canned fish are tuna, salmon, sardines, mackerel and pilchards. They may be canned in vegetable oil, tomato sauce or brine. Some brands of canned fish are free from additives, but others contain **flavouring, flavour enhancers** and **salt**.

canned fruit A fruit that has been canned to preserve it, increase its shelf-life and to make seasonal fruits available all the year round. Fruit may be canned in heavy or light syrup, or in its own juice, natural juice or water. Canned fruit may have natural or artificial **colouring** added as well as **flavourings**.

canned vegetables Vegetables that have been canned to preserve them, increase their shelf-life and to make seasonal vegetables available all the year round. Canning beans, such as haricot, kidney and butter beans and peas such as chickpeas, removes the need for long slow soaking and cooking that is otherwise necessary to make them edible.

canning A well-established method of preserving food, traditionally prone to few problems except perhaps tainting of food from the tin-plate that lines the can – and then usually only after very long periods of storage. Even this can be minimized by the use of **sequestrants** or by coating the inside of the can with lacquer; aluminium cans, favoured for fizzy drinks, are always lacquered. Food poisoning by anaerobic organisms (such as **Salmonella**) is a very remote, but nevertheless dangerous, possibility. More common problems include the destruction of **vitamins** by the canning process, and the loss of colour, flavour and texture of canned fruit and vegetables. These losses are compensated for by the use of vitamin supplements, **anti-browning agents**, **colours**, **flavours** and **firming agents**. **Emulsifiers**, **stabilizers** and **thickeners** are also common ingredients in composite canned foods such as soups. Thickeners may also be added to canned pie fillings and the liquid in canned meats.

canthaxanthin (E161g)   An orange **carotenoid** pigment that occurs naturally in some fish, mushrooms and shellfish, but which is usually synthesized for use in the food industry. It is sometimes fed to trout and salmon in fish farms to increase the pinkness of their flesh. It is also employed as a **colouring** agent in a variety of products, including jellies, margarine, pickles, sauces, sweets and the breadcrumbs on chicken pieces and fish fingers. In very large quantities, canthaxanthin may affect the retina of the eye, as reported in people who have used it in edible suntan capsules for dyeing the skin.

caper A trailing Mediterranean cappa-
ridaceous shrub. Its flower buds are used as a
spicy flavouring, usually pickled in brine. It is
traditionally used to flavour mayonnaise and
the sauce served with boiled mutton.

capsanthin (E160c; also called **capsorubin**;
paprika extract; **paprika oleoresin**) A hot
spicy extract of European red pepper (cap-
sicum or paprika), employed mainly as a red-
orange **colouring** agent. It is fed to chickens to
darken the colour of egg yolks and is used in
chicken pies, fish products and processed
cheese.

capsorubin Alternative name for **capsanthin**.

caramel (E150; also called **caramel
colour**) The most commonly used **colouring**
agent in food, to which it imparts a dark brown
or black colour. It is made by the controlled
heat treatment of glucose and various other
sugars. Acids, alkalis, ammonia and sulphur
compounds may be used in its preparation, but
not always. Caustic (i.e. alkaline) caramel is
used to colour some brandy and whisky,
ammonia caramel is an ingredient of beer (particularly stout) and gravy browning, and
sulphite-ammonia caramel is favoured for cola
drinks and malt vinegar. Other foods containing caramel include biscuits, brown bread,

61

cakes, chocolate products, crisps, fish pastes, pickles, sauces, soups and sweets.

Some bowel problems have been reported in volunteers who were fed sulphite-ammonia caramel. Caramel cannot be added to bread in the US and many European countries, although the practice is permitted in the UK. There has been concern that it should be possible to identify which type of caramel is in the product, consequently more explicit labelling is likely. The 1987 **Food Advisory Committee** report on colour proposed a maximum content of caramel in certain specified foods.

caraway seed The aromatic seed of a Eurasian umbelliferous plant, with a liquorice taste. It is used as a flavouring mainly in cakes, biscuits and bread.

carbohydrate Any of a group of organic compounds including **starch**, **polysaccharides** and sugars, important sources of energy for the body. They are broken down into their component simple sugars during digestion: starches into **glucose**; **sucrose** into glucose and **fructose**; **lactose** into glucose and galactose. These simple sugars are either **metabolized** by the body immediately or stored as glycogen or body fat.

carbon black (E153; also called **vegetable carbon)** A pure form of carbon made from charcoal (usually of plant origin), employed as a black **colouring** agent. It is used in chocolate cakes, fruit juices, jams, jellies and liquorice. It is banned in the US because of the fear that **carcinogenic** chemicals could be produced during its manufacture.

carbon dioxide (E290)   A colourless, odourless gas that is present in small amounts in the air. It is formed by the decomposition and combustion of organic compounds and during respiration. It is also produced by any fermentation process, usually through the action of **yeast** (as in the production of bread, beer and wine), or by the action of an **acid** on a carbonate or **hydrogen carbonate** (bicarbonate).

In bread-making, it is the generation of carbon dioxide gas that makes the bread rise. Similarly, carbonates and hydrogen carbonates are used in **raising agents**, because the carbon dioxide they produce in the presence of acids causes foods to rise, e.g. cakes. Carbon dioxide is also the gas in fizzy, or carbonated, drinks – including some wines and canned or bottled beers – and in this application it is an **aerator**. Its presence acts as a **preservative** in some fruit juices, and it is employed as an inert gas (instead of air) inside the packaging of some foods such as cream to prevent or delay oxidation. Liquid carbon dioxide (under pressure) and solid carbon dioxide (dry ice) are used as **coolants** and **freezants**.

carboxymethylcellulose, sodium salt (E466; also called carmellose sodium; CMC) A common food additive with many uses. It is used as a **gelling agent** and **thickening agent**, and also to modify the texture of foods. It is an indigestible **bulking agent** and **stabilizer** for foams. It is used in various fillings and toppings; in dips, sauces, spreads and soups; in custard, ice cream and milk shakes; and in instant drinks and instant mashed potato.

carcinogen A substance that can cause **cancer**. See also **carcinogenicity test**.

carcinogenicity test A scientific test to establish whether or not a substance is a **carcinogen**. Tests are usually carried out using experimental animals, including rodents, rabbits, dogs and pigs. The substance is usually administered in large doses over a period of time, and the animals are then killed and dissected to detect traces of tumours or other cancerous changes. A substance that is carcinogenic in animals does not necessarily have the same effect (especially in smaller doses) in human beings, although such a possibility is usually taken very seriously.

cardamon (also called **cardamum; cardamom**) An aromatic spice made from the seeds of a tropical Asian plant of the ginger family. It is a common constituent of curry and is also used in pickles, soups and non-savoury foods, e.g. bread, buns, biscuits and cakes.

carmine of cochineal Alternative name for **cochineal**.

carminic acid Alternative name for **cochineal**.

carmoisine (E122; also called azorubine) An **azo dye** employed as a **colouring** agent, used to impart a red colour to foods. It withstands heat treatment, which is useful in foods that need such processing after fermentation. It is found in desserts, jams, jellies, sauces, sausages, soups, sweets and yoghurts, and in packet breadcrumbs. It is not recommended for people with **asthma** or **aspirin sensitivity** and children with a history of **hyperactivity**. It has been banned in Canada, Japan, Norway, Sweden and the US.

carnauba wax (903) A hard yellow or tan wax that occurs as a coating on the young leaves of the Brazilian wax palm, used as a **glazing agent** and polishing agent to put a shine on citrus fruits and sweets.

carob gum Alternative name for **locust bean gum**.

carotene (E160a) This **carotenoid** pigment exists in three forms, termed alpha-, beta- and gamma-carotene. They are yellow to red in colour and found in all plants, especially apricots, carrots, oranges and tomatoes. For commercial use they are extracted from carrots, lucerne (alfalfa) or red palm oil, or they can be synthesized in the laboratory. In the body, carotenes are converted to **vitamin A**. For this reason they are added as a supplement to margarines and milk products. They are used as **colouring** agents in some cheeses, desserts, soft drinks and pre-packed cakes.

carotenoid A member of a group of naturally occurring plant pigments, of which the **carotenes** and **xanthophylls** are typical. Many of them can also be produced synthetically.

carrageenan (E407; also called **carrageen**; **Irish moss)** A very widely used **gelling agent** and **thickener** made from various species of red seaweed. It is also employed as a **stabilizer**. Chemically it resembles cellulose and **starch** because, like them, it is a **polysaccharide**. It is used in many kinds of milk-based foods and drinks, cheeses, meat pies, jams and jellies.

cassia The aromatic bark of a tropical Asian tree of the laurel family, used as a spice with a flavour resembling that of **cinnamon**. It is used very much like cinnamon, but it is less suitable for use in sweet dishes.

caustic potash Alternative name for **potassium hydroxide**.

caustic soda Alternative name for **sodium hydroxide**.

cayenne pepper (also called **red pepper**) A very hot spice and condiment made from the dried fruits and seeds of various capsicums (tropical American plants related to the tomato and potato). It is used sparingly to flavour meats and sauces, particularly barbecued or devilled dishes. It gives no colour to food when used in such small amounts.

celery salt Finely powdered salt containing ground **celery seed**, used as a flavouring on salads and in cooking, particularly egg dishes.

celery seed The dried seeds of celery, an umbelliferous Eurasian plant, used for flavouring savoury foods, e.g. pickles, salads, bread, meat and fish dishes.

cell mediated See **delayed allergy**.

chalk Alternative name for **calcium carbonate**.

67

chamomile An alternative name for **camomile**.

cheese The curd of milk separated from the whey. In the most common cheese-making method, used particularly to make Cheddar cheese, the milk is pasteurized to destroy any harmful bacteria. A starter culture is added together with **rennet** and the resulting curd is then stirred, scalded, drained, salted and pressed. Finally, it is stored at a constant temperature for a period from a few weeks to several months.

Some cheeses such as fat-reduced, cottage cheese, curd and Edam are made with skimmed milk, others are made from goats' or sheep milk. Salt is added to all types of cheese in varying amounts. The preservatives **nisin** and **sorbic acid** are allowed in hard cheeses, as are certain natural colours such as **annatto** and **carotene** or their synthetic equivalents. The preservatives **sodium nitrate** and **sodium nitrite** are permitted in all cheeses with the exception of Cheddar, Cheshire and soft cheese. Products labelled 'cheese flavoured' must by law contain cheese, whereas those labelled 'cheese flavour' need only contain an artificial flavour, that imitates cheese taste.

chelating agent A substance that binds chemically to metals, particularly heavy metals such as copper, iron, manganese, nickel and zinc. Chelating agents are used as **sequestrants** to 'mop up' traces of such metals in foods, perhaps present because the food has inevitably come into contact with processing machinery.

chervil An umbelliferous Eurasian plant with a sweet delicate aniseed flavour, whose leaves are used as a herb to give flavour to salads, sauces and soups.

children There are certain additives that are not permitted by law in foods made specifically for babies and young children. These are: **antioxidants** E310, E311, E312, E320, E321; all **artificial sweeteners**; **preservatives** E250 and E251; **flavour enhancers** 621, 622, 623, 627, 631, 635, and all **colouring**, with the exception of the three colours that are vitamins (**beta-carotene**, **riboflavin** and **riboflavin–5'-phosphate**).

Many of these additives are found in foods not manufactured specifically for children but consumed by them, often in large quantities. Such products include sausages, fish fingers, crisps, soft drinks and confectionery.

Some children who are allergic to certain foods are also allergic to some additives, notably artificial colourings and preservatives. **Hyperactivity** in children has been strongly linked with the presence of additives in the diet and treatment of such children often involves the total exclusion of certain additives. See also **Feingold diet**.

Chile saltpetre Alternative name for **sodium nitrate**.

chilli powder A very hot spice made from the ground dried seed pods of red capsicums, sometimes including other spices, used for flavouring pickles and savoury sauces. Mild chilli powder or chilli seasoning contains a mixture of spices and is less hot.

Chinese restaurant syndrome A disorder characterized by dizziness, headache, nausea, palpitations, thirst and a numbness in the neck and hands. It has been associated in some sensitive people with the flavour enhancer **monosodium glutamate**, commonly used in soy sauce and other Chinese foods; as well as many manufactured non-Chinese dishes such as soups and meat dishes. It may be an example of a **food intolerance** to glutamates. See also **food allergy**.

chives A savoury flavouring made from the hollow leaves of a Eurasian plant of the onion family. It is used to flavour salads and dressings and as a garnish to soup and savoury dishes.

chlorine (925) A poisonous gas employed as a **bleaching agent** for flour. It can therefore be found in baked products and can affect the vitamin content, particularly vitamin E. It is also used as a disinfectant to destroy bacteria and fungi, as in the chlorination of drinking water and, in larger doses, swimming pools.

chlorine dioxide (926; also called chlorine peroxide) A poisonous gas employed as a **bleaching agent** and bactericide. It is used to bleach flour, fats, oils and waxes and in purifying drinking water. It is also an **improving agent** for flour, although it reacts with and reduces the amount of vitamin E present in flour. It is found in baked products. Chlorine dioxide is banned in many European countries, but not in the UK.

chlorine peroxide Alternative name for **chlorine dioxide**.

chlorophyll (E140; also called natural green 3) The photosynthetic pigment in all green plants, from which it is extracted using **solvents** to produce a rather unstable green **colouring** agent. The main plants used commercially are clover, grass, lucerne (alfalfa), nettles and spinach. Chlorophyll is used to colour ice cream, soups and sweets.

chocolate A form of confectionery made from cocoa. Sugar, cocoa and cocoa butter are the basic ingredients of most chocolate. **Flavourings** and the emulsifier **lecithin** may also be added. As with other types of confectionery, chocolates and novelty chocolate bars may contain **colourings**. Products labelled 'chocolate flavoured' must by law contain chocolate, whereas those labelled 'chocolate flavour' need only contain an artificial flavour that imitates chocolate taste.

chocolate brown HT Alternative name for **brown HT**.

cholecalciferol Alternative name for **vitamin D**.

cholesterol A fatty substance that occurs naturally in all animal tissues, including the bloodstream. It is used by the body to synthesize bile acids and hormones. It is produced mainly in the liver, but also occurs in various foods, particularly those rich in animal fats. High levels of cholesterol in the blood have been associated with atherosclerosis, which is the build-up of fatty deposits on the inner walls of arteries.

choline An organic **base** that occurs in egg yolk and in the human body, where it is concerned with the deposition of fat in the liver. Its compound acetylcholine plays a key role in the normal transmission of nerve impulses.

chutney A pickle originally from India, made from various fruits and/or vegetables and containing vinegar, spices and often sugar. Commercial chutneys may also contain various additives, such as **artificial sweeteners**, **colours** and **thickeners**.

CI Number Alternative name for **Colour Index Number**.

cider An **alcoholic drink** made by fermenting apple juice using yeast. It can be made dry or sweet, with added sugar. Commercial cider may contain similar additives to those found in **beer**, such as **foam stabilizers** and **sulphur dioxide**. As with other alcoholic drinks, cider with an alcoholic strength by volume of more than 1.2% does not have to give an ingredient list on the label or can.

cider vinegar A type of **vinegar** made by brewing and fermenting cider, the taste of which is retained in the finished product. Cider vinegar can be used in pickling and in vinaigrette dressings.

cinnamon An aromatic spice made from the yellow-brown bark of a tropical Asian tree of the laurel family. It is used as a flavouring in a wide variety of sweet and spicy baked goods, and to flavour hot drinks, mulled wines and punches.

citric acid (E330)   An **organic acid** that occurs naturally in various fruits, particularly lemons and other citrus fruits. Most citric acid for the food industry is made from molasses by a fermentation process.

Citric acid has many uses. It is an **acidity regulator** and **buffer**; it prevents discoloration and the deterioration of flavour of canned fruit, and is a **flavouring** in its own right; it is a **sequestrant** in wine-making, where it 'mops up' iron and prevents it forming compounds with **tannins** that could make the wine cloudy; and it acts as a **synergist** for **antioxidants**. It is also added to jams to help them to set (traditionally lemons were used for this purpose). It is likely to be found in almost any food or drink containing fruit. It is also used in various cheese products, frozen fish and frozen potato products, jams, jellies and packet cake and soup mixes, among many others.

citric acid esters of mono- and diglycerides of fatty acids (E472c; also called **citroglycerides)**   Prepared synthetically by reacting **citric acid** with **esters** of **glycerol** (glycerine), these substances are employed as **emulsifiers** and **stabilizers** in such products as dessert toppings, ice cream and soups.

citric acid triammonium salt   Alternative name for **triammonium citrate**.

citroglycerides Alternative name for **citric acid esters of mono- and diglycerides of fatty acids**.

clove An aromatic spice made from the dried flower buds of an evergreen tree of the myrtle family, native to the East Indies but now also cultivated in tropical Africa. Cloves are used whole or as a ground powder to flavour apple dishes, mincemeat and bread sauce.

CMC Abbreviation of **carboxymethyl-cellulose**.

coal tar dye (also called **aniline dye**) A member of a group of synthetic dyes employed as **colouring** agents, so named because the first of such dyes were made from aniline and other chemicals found in coal tar. They include **brilliant blue FCF**, **erythrosine**, **indigo carmine**, **patent blue V**, **quinoline yellow** and all the **azo dyes**. Some coal tar dyes have been shown to cause an allergic reaction in people who are sensitive to them, and as a group the dyes are not recommended for children who display **hyperactivity**; some of them are banned in various countries.

coating agent A substance added in the form of a fine powder to the surface of a food to prevent stickiness. For example, chewing gum is often coated with **calcium silicate** powder. It has a similar action to that of an **anti-caking agent**.

cobalt A metallic element, a constituent of **vitamin B₁₂** (cyanocobalamine) and therefore an essential trace element in the diet. Liver is a good food source. Salts of cobalt were used as foaming agents in beers until it was discovered that alcohol increased the toxic effects of excessive cobalt intake.

cochineal (E120; also called **carmine of cochineal**; **carminic acid**; **natural red 4)** An expensive natural red **colouring** agent that is extracted from the bodies of pregnant beetle-like, cactus-eating scale insects. It is employed commercially in a water-soluble form (ammonium carmine) and an insoluble form (calcium carmine). The former is used in alcoholic and soft drinks, red-veined cheese, sauces, sausage skins, desserts and sweets. Insoluble carmine is used in cakes and biscuits (e.g. in icing), desserts and soups. It is not recommended for children with **hyperactivity**. It is banned in Norway and Spain.

coeliac disease A disorder in which food is not absorbed properly because the intestinal lining is abnormally sensitive to **gluten**, a substance present in wheat rye and to a lesser degree oats and barley. This may in turn lead to malnutrition and vitamin deficiency disorders. It is most common in children, although it does occur in adults. Treatment is with a diet that contains absolutely no gluten, and gluten-free products are available for this purpose.

coffee A beverage made from boiling water and the ground, roasted seeds (beans) of the coffee tree, of which there are several varieties grown in tropical regions throughout the world. The taste of a particular type of coffee depends on the blend of beans and how they are roasted (and indeed on how the drink is made). Coffee contains **caffeine** and other alkaloids, although **decaffeinated** versions are available. See also **instant coffee**.

cologel Alternative name for **methylcellulose**.

Colour Index Number (also called **CI Number**) A reference number for specifying a colour as set out in the Colour Index of the Society of Dyers and Colourists.

colouring The food industry's term for any colouring agent, artificial or natural. Colourings are also referred to as dyes and pigments. They are used to restore the original colour to foods after processing, or to make colourless or pale foods look more appetizing. **Artificial colours** include **azo dyes** and **coal tar dyes**. Commonly used **natural colours** include **annatto**, **anthocyanins**, **beetroot red**, **caramel**, **carotenes**, **chlorophyll**, **cochineal**, **crocin**, **curcumin** and **xanthophylls**, although many of these are also produced synthetically (when they are called nature-identical). There is, however, no guarantee that a natural (or nature-identical) colour is necessarily safer than an artificial one. See also **bleaching agents**; **food allergy**; **hyperactivity**.

colouring matter The official term for a water-soluble or oil-soluble, artificial or natural **colouring** agent, usually referred to in the food industry as simply a colour.

Colouring Matter in Food Regulations A set of regulations issued by the Ministry of Agriculture, Fisheries and Food that control the use of **colouring** matter in food. The regulations list the substances that are permitted and where appropriate they specify the foods in which they may be used.

comfrey A Eurasian plant of the borage family whose fresh leaves are used in salads or dried to make a tisane or infusion.

Committee on the Medical Aspects of Food

Policy (COMA) The Department of Health's central advisory committee on food and health.

Committee on Toxicity of Chemicals in Food, Consumer Products and the Environment (COT) The committee of the Department of Health which reports also to the Ministry of Agriculture, Fisheries and Food, usually via its **Food Advisory Committee** (FAC). It considers evidence about the safety of new and existing food additives, recommends for or against their use and if necessary sets maximum limits on the quantities that can be used.

confectionery A large variety of sweet-tasting products usually with a high sugar content and negligible nutrient value. Many types of additives may be used in the manufacture of confectionery, including **colouring, flavourings, acidity regulators, glazing agents, antioxidants** and **emulsifiers**.

contact dermatitis A skin disorder, often a form of allergy, caused by contact with an irritating substance (**allergen**). Food additives that can cause it in susceptible people include **benzoic acid** and benzoates, and the gum **tragacanth**.

convenience food A food that is easy to prepare, usually pre-packed (canned, dehydrated or frozen) and often pre-cooked. It should be distinguished from a snack food, which is ready for immediate consumption without any preparation at all. A tin of soup is a convenience food, whereas a hamburger is a snack. Despite their poor reputation, many convenience foods are produced using ingredients and methods that result in a dish which is nutritionally better than one with less fresh ingredients and which has been subjected to prolonged home cooking.

convenience meal Alternative name for **ready meal**.

cooking fat A fat intended for incorporating into prepared foods, such as pastry, or for use in actual cooking, such as deep or shallow frying. It may be completely natural and of animal origin, as are lard and suet, or manufactured from vegetable oil in much the same way as **margarine**. But unlike margarine, cooking fat contains little or no water.

coolant A substance such as liquid or solid **carbon dioxide** that is used to keep foods cool during manufacture or storage.

copper complexes of chlorophyll and chlorphyllins (E141; also called **copper phaeophytins)** Green or olive-green **colouring** agents made from **chlorophyll** by replacing the magnesium it normally contains (as part of its molecular structure) with copper. They are used to colour green vegetables, fruit, ice cream, soups and sage Derby cheese.

coriander An aromatic umbelliferous plant from Europe whose leaves are used as a herb to give flavour to salads and soups.

coriander seed A spice made from the dried ripe seeds of the **coriander** plant. It has a mild, sweet orange-like flavour and is available whole or as a powder. It is used in curry powders and pickling spices and a wide variety of other foods.

cornflour The finely ground kernel of the cereal maize or Indian corn. Cornflour is almost pure **starch** and is used to thicken sauces and gravies.

corn sugar gum Alternative name for **xanthin gum**.

corn syrup A sugary syrup made from maize or cornstarch; it consists mainly of **glucose**.

COT Abbreviation of **Committee on Toxicity of Chemicals in Food**.

costmary Alternative name for **alecost**.

cream The fat that rises to the top of the milk and which can be skimmed off. Regulations for the composition of cream are based on the minimum fat contents. Clotted cream and Devonshire cream have a minimum fat content of 55%, double cream 48%, whipped, whipping and sour cream 35%, sterilized cream 23%, single cream 18% and half cream 12%. Certain **emulsifiers** and **stabilizers** are permitted in whipped cream and sterilized cream, sugar in whipped cream and the preservative **nisin** in clotted and canned cream, otherwise additives are not permitted in cream of any type. See also **artificial cream**; **butter**; **ice cream**.

cream of tartar   Alternative name for **monopotassium L-(+)-tartrate**.

cream substitute   See **artificial cream**.

crisping agent   Alternative name for **firming agent**.

crisps   Thin slices of potato, fried and eaten as a popular snack food. Crisps have a high fat content and usually contain **antioxidants** to prevent the fat going rancid. They may also contain added salt, **flavourings**, **flavour enhancer**, **colouring** and **preservatives**.

crocin (also called **saffron**)   A yellow dye used to colour or add a spicy flavour to food. It is a **carotenoid** pigment found in the stigmas of crocus flowers and the seeds of gardenia, from which it is obtained by extraction with **solvents**. It is used to colour batter and cakes.

cryptoxanthin (E161c)   A yellow plant pigment, one of the **xanthophylls**, that occurs in marigolds and in the flowers and fruits of the Cape gooseberry, a plant of the tomato family.

cumin (also called **cummin**)   An aromatic umbelliferous plant from the Mediterranean region with a slightly bitter taste. Its dried seeds, sold whole or as a powder, are used as a spice and condiment. Cumin is used as an ingredient in curry powders and the seeds are used in chutney and pickles.

curcumin (E100)   A yellow **colouring** agent that is obtained by **solvent** extraction from the spice **turmeric**. Because it is a natural substance, it is favoured over **azo dyes** and other **artificial colours**. Its yellow colour tends to turn orange in **alkaline** conditions, and is not very stable to light. It is used to restore the colour to margarine, butter, cheese, ice cream, fish cakes and fish fingers, curry powder and savoury rice, salad dressings, soups and sweets.

curing   A method of preserving food, particularly fish or meat, by treating it with **salt** or **saltpetre**. Often the food is also smoked (see

smoked fish), and the term curing is occasionally used to describe smoking without any sort of salt treatment.

curry powder A powdered mixture of hot spices, traditionally of Indian origin, used to flavour sauces for rice, meat and vegetable dishes. Typical spices used in curry include cardamon, chillis, cumin, ginger, pepper and turmeric. Commercial curry powders may also contain various colours, preservatives and other additives.

custard powder A mixture consisting mainly of **cornflour**, with added salt, **flavourings** and yellow **colouring** agent (typically **annatto**), to which hot milk or water is added to make custard.

cyanadin (163a) A natural red **anthocyanin** pigment, used as a colouring agent.

cyclamate An **artificial sweetener**, not currently used in the UK.

L-cysteine hydrochloride (920) An **amino acid**, available also as a monohydrate, made from animal hair and feathers. It is employed as an **improving agent** for flour and as a chicken flavouring in stock cubes.

L-cysteine hydrochloride monohydrate An **amino acid (920)** made from animal hair and feathers. It is employed as an **improving agent** for flour and as a chicken flavouring in stock cubes.

dairy ice cream An ice cream that contains milk fat, although not necessarily as cream. Butter, or where the water has been removed, butter oil, may be used. Dairy ice cream may contain **flavouring** and **colouring** as well as **emulsifiers**.

dairy spread A paste used as a spreading alternative to **butter** and **margarine**. Dairy spreads are made from **cream** or **buttermilk** which is blended with **vegetable oil** to give a taste of butter rather than margarine. Such products can be used straight from the fridge. They contain added **salt**, **emulsifiers**, **flavouring** and **colouring**.

datemark Nearly all pre-packed foods with a shelf life of less than 18 months must bear a **best before date**, a **sell by date** or a **use by date**. Exceptions include fresh fruit and vegetables, frozen foods, cheeses (which improve with keeping), salt, sugar, wines and most other alcoholic drinks and vinegar.

DDS Abbreviation of **dioctyl sodium sulphosuccinate**.

decaffeinated coffee Coffee from which most of the **caffeine** has been removed using a

solvent, usually **dichloromethane**. The solvent itself is then removed by steaming, although a residue of up to 10 parts per million can remain.

decaffeinated tea Tea from which most of the **caffeine** has been removed using a **solvent**, usually **dichloromethane**. The solvent itself is then removed by steaming, although a residue of up to 10 parts per million can remain.

dehydration The removal of water from a substance, employed as a method of preserving food. The process involves heating the food in a hot airstream or in vacuum driers. Milk and other liquid foods (such as beverages and soups) can be dried by spraying them into a heated chamber.

All dehydrated foods – including 'instant' foods – must obviously be packed and kept in perfectly watertight containers. They are reconstituted by adding or soaking in water. The result may lack the colour and texture of the original, and the vitamin content may be affected. In composite foods, various additives such as **colouring** agents and **flavourings** may be included to compensate for these shortcomings. See also **dried food**; **freeze drying**.

delayed allergy An allergic reaction that occurs some time after exposure to the **allergen**. See **food allergy**.

delphinidin (E163b) A natural blue **antho-cyanin** pigment, used as a colouring agent.

delta-tocopherol, synthetic (E309; also called **vitamin E)** A synthetic form of vitamin E, employed as a vitamin supplement and as an **antioxidant**, particularly for fats. It is found in sausages, but does not tolerate freezing.

dextrin (also called **starch gum; starch sugar)** A soluble sugary substance produced when **starch** is heated (e.g. toasting bread), or treated with strong acids or by the action of enzymes (e.g. during digestion). It forms a gum with water, and is used as a **thickener**.

dextrose Alternative name for **glucose**.

diabetes (also called **diabetes mellitus)** A disorder in which a person's pancreas does not produce enough insulin to control the levels of the sugar glucose in the blood, which may 'spill over' and appear also in the urine. In some diabetics the pancreas produces no insulin, and such people need regular injections of the hormone. In others some insulin is produced, and the disorder can be controlled with a low-carbohydrate diet and, possibly, tablets. All diabetics are encouraged to avoid high sugar diets and to eat more starchy and fibrous foods. **Sorbitol** or an **artificial sweetener** can be used to give sweetness to the diet. Special diabetic foods are also available.

diacetin Alternative name for **glycerol diacetate**.

diacetyltartaric acid esters of mono- and diglycerides of fatty acids (E472e) Synthetic compounds used as **emulsifiers** and **stabilizers** in brown bread, chocolate mixes, crisps, frozen pizza, gravy granules and soups.

diarrhoea Frequent passing of watery faeces, caused by gastero-enteric inflammation or irritation, possibly resulting from contaminated food, overambitious use of spices, or a toxic chemical. It may also be a symptom of a **food allergy** (see **Chinese restaurant syndrome**). Certain food additives, such as **ascorbic acid** (vitamin C), sulphite-ammonia **caramel** and **tragacanth**, can cause diarrhoea in susceptible people. See also **bowel problems**.

dicalcium citrate (E333) A calcium salt of **citric acid**, used as a **buffer**, **firming agent**, **emulsifier** and **sequestrant**. See **calcium citrate**.

dicalcium diphosphate (540; also called dicalcium pyrophosphate) A calcium salt of orthophosphoric acid (see **calcium hydrogen orthophosphate** for a note on naming), employed as a **buffer** and **acidity regulator**, dietary supplement (to supply calcium and phosphorus), conditioner for dough and yeast nutrient. It occurs in some bread, processed cheeses and potato crisps.

dicalcium pyrophosphate Alternative name for **dicalcium diphosphate**.

dichlorodifluoromethane (also called **Freon–12**) A **solvent** that is a type of CFC (chlorofluorocarbon), used also as a refrigerant and as an aerosol propellant. It can be found in **decaffeinated coffee** and spice extracts where it has been used for extraction purposes.

dichloromethane (also called **methylene chloride**) A chlorinated hydrocarbon **solvent** used to extract **natural colours** and to remove **caffeine** from decaffeinated coffee.

diethyl ether (also called **ether**; **ethoxyethane**) A volatile and highly flammable organic **solvent**, formerly used as an anaesthetic. It is used in food processing to obtain natural extracts.

Dijon mustard A creamy greyish-yellow mustard with a subtle flavour. It is blended with salt, spices and white wine or verjuice (the acidic juice obtained from unripe green grapes). Dijon mustard is used in vinaigrette dressings, mayonnaise and creamy sauces.

dill An aromatic umbelliferous plant native to Eurasia, whose feathery leaves are used as a herb. Dill has a mild caraway flavour, and is used particularly with salmon and to flavour pickles.

dill seed The seed-like fruits of the **dill** plant, used as a savoury flavouring. They have a more pungent flavour than the herb.

diluent A substance used to dissolve or dilute other food additives; a **solvent**.

dimethicone Alternative name for **dimethylpolysiloxane**.

dimethylpolysiloxane (**900**; also called **dimethicone**; **simethicone**) A synthetic mixture of the silicone compound dimethylpolysiloxane and silica gel (**silicon dioxide**), employed as an **anti-caking agent** in powdered milk and as an **anti-foaming agent** (particularly in brewing) because of its water-repellent properties. It is also used as a base for chewing gum because it is totally inert and indigestible. It may be found in fruit juices, jams, molasses, soft drinks, soups and syrups, to which it is added to prevent frothing or foaming during manufacture.

dioctyl sodium sulphosuccinate (also called **DSS**) An **emulsifier** and **stabilizer**, added to an emulsion (or powder that is mixed with water to form an emulsion) to prevent the droplets of oil from coming together and separating out. It is found in cheeses and powdered soft drink mixes.

diphenyl Alternative name for **biphenyl**.

dipotassium hydrogen orthophosphate (E340b; also called **dipotassium phosphate**, or **DKP**; **potassium phosphate dibasic**) An acid salt of **orthophosphoric acid**, employed as a **buffer** and **sequestrant**. It is also used as a **synergist** for **antioxidants**, as an **emulsifier** and as a source of phosphorus in yeast foods for brewing and wine-making. It is found in powdered milk; mixes for making cream, custard, drinking chocolate or ice cream; and cooked and cured meat.

dipotassium L-(+)-tartrate (E336) A salt of **tartaric acid**, employed as a **buffer** and **emulsifier**. It is also used as an **antioxidant** and as a **synergist** for other anitoxidants. It is found in jams, jellies and packet dessert mixes.

disaccharide A type of **sugar** that consists of two simpler (**monosaccharide**) units. For example, **sucrose** is made up of one **fructose** and one

glucose unit chemically joined together. Disaccharides are therefore usually sweeter and have higher calorific values than monosaccharides.

disodium citrate (E331b) A salt of **citric acid**, employed as a **buffer** and **emulsifier**. It is also used as an **antioxidant** and as a **synergist** for other antioxidants. It is found in fizzy drinks, jellies, pickles, processed cheese and some wines.

disodium dihydrogen diphosphate (E450a; also called **tetrasodium pyrophosphate)** A salt of pyrophosphoric acid, employed as a **buffer** and **emulsifier**, and as a **gelling agent** and **stabilizer** in dessert toppings and other dried milk products. It is also found in cheese products, fish fingers, fruit pies, meat pies and other meat products, including burgers and sausages.

disodium hydrogen orthophosphate (E339b) An acid salt of **orthophosphoric acid** with a wide range of uses. It is a **buffer**, **gelling agent**, **stabilizer** and a **synergist** for **antioxidants**. It also hastens the penetration of salt into cured meats. It is found in fizzy drinks; sausages, ham and other cooked meats; and in products made from processed cheese. See **calcium hydrogen orthophosphate**.

disodium L-(+)-tartrate (E333; also called **sodium L-(+)-tartrate)** A **buffer**, **emulsifier**

and **sequestrant**, which is also employed as an **antioxidant** and as a **synergist** for other antioxidants. It is used in jams, jellies, soft drinks and sweets.

distilled vinegar A colourless vinegar usually distilled from **malt vinegar**. Distilled vinegar is used particularly for pickling where the colour is important, for example in pickled silver onions.

diuretic A substance that stimulates the kidneys to produce more urine, so that extra water (and salts) are excreted. Some foods and drinks are mild diuretics, e.g. tea and coffee because of their caffeine content. A few food additives are also mild diuretics such as the preservatives **formic (methanoic) acid** and **sodium formate** (methanoate) if taken in sufficiently large quantities.

DKP Abbreviation and alternative name for **dipotassium hydrogen orthophosphate**.

dodecyl gallate (E312; also called **dodecyl 3,4,5-trihydroxybenzoate**) An **antioxidant**, used in margarine and various other fats and oils. It may be used in combination with other gallates. It is not recommended for people with **asthma** or **aspirin sensitivity**, nor for children who display **hyperactivity**. Dodecyl gallate is banned in foods for babies and young children, and totally banned in the US.

dried food A food that has had its water content reduced as a method of preservation. In the case of **dried fruit**, the product can be eaten as it is, but in others, such as dried milk, vegetables and soups, the product must be reconstituted to make it edible. See also **dehydration**; **freeze drying**.

dried fruit A fruit that has had its water content reduced to preserve it, increase its shelf-life and make seasonal or tropical fruits available all the year round. Fruit may be sun-dried or it may undergo more rapid heat treatment. **Mineral hydrocarbons** are permitted on the surface of dried fruit to prevent the pieces sticking together when packaged, but the use of mineral hydrocarbons in food is at present under discussion. **Sulphur dioxide** may be used to preserve the colour, and dried fruit treated in this way should be avoided by people with **asthma**.

DSS Abbreviation and alternative name for **dioctyl sodium sulphosuccinate**.

dykon Alternative name for **sodium hydrogen diacetate**.

eczema A skin disorder that sometimes has

an allergic origin. It may be a form of **contact dermatitis**, or in its atopic form be caused by a **food allergy**. Foods which are commonly found to cause eczema are cows' milk, eggs, wheat, shellfish, fish and nuts.

edible bone phosphate (E542)   Essentially an impure form of calcium phosphate, made from animal bones. It is employed as an **anti-caking agent** and dietary mineral supplement to supply calcium and phosphorus. It is also used as a filler (i.e. an inert bulking ingredient) in making tablets.

edible gum   One of a number of substances extracted from the seeds and sap of certain trees and used by food and confectionery manufacturers as **thickeners** and **stabilizers**. Examples of edible gums include **carob gum**, **guar gum** and **gum arabic**.

egg   The oval or round reproductive body laid by female birds and other animals. Hens' eggs are the most common eggs consumed in Britain, but others such as duck, goose and quail eggs are also popular.

Most eggs are produced by battery hens, but free-range and barn-laid eggs are also available. Colour such as **tartrazine** may be added to battery hen food to encourage a deep yellow yolk, and antibiotics may also be added as a prevention against disease. Hens' eggs are sold by class and size. Class A eggs have not been refrigerated or preserved and the shells have not been cleaned in any way. Class B eggs may be washed or cleaned. They may also have been refrigerated or preserved by oiling or storing in gas or water glass. Class C eggs are used only by food manufacturers. Sizing of eggs is by number: grade 1 weigh 70 g; grade 2 weigh 65–70 g; grade 3 weigh 60–65 g; grade 4 weigh 55–60 g; grade 5 weigh 50–55 g.

emulsifier A substance that causes water or a water-based liquid to combine with a fat or oil to form a stable **emulsion**. Emulsifiers include natural substances, such as gums and cellulose derivatives (e.g. **alginates**, **lecithins** and **tragacanth**), and synthetic ones (e.g. various **glycerol** esters, such as stearates and other soap-like compounds).

Emulsifiers are essential in the manufacture of several foods, e.g. margarine, salad cream and packet soups and other convenience foods. They are employed for a variety of purposes in many other food products: to prevent caking in coffee whiteners; to thicken puddings; in soft drinks to prevent particles from joining together; to inhibit the staling of bread. Emulsifiers are also used to help incorporate air into liquids, often in combination with **stabilizers** to prevent the mixture separating.

Emulsifiers and Stabilizers in Food Regulations A set of regulations issued by the Ministry of Agriculture, Fisheries and Food that control the use of **emulsifiers** and **stabilizers** in food. The regulations list the substances that are permitted. Where appropriate, they specify the food in which they may be used and the maximum levels that may be added. They also list certain foods in which the use of permitted emulsifiers and stabilizers is limited.

emulsifier YN Alternative name for **ammonium phosphatides**.

emulsifying salt A type of salt (e.g. a citrate or tartrate) that is added to such foods as melted cheese during processing to prevent them forming plastic-like strands when heated. Some emulsifying salts also act as **emulsifiers**.

emulsion An intimate mixture of oily and watery substances that does not settle out into two layers when left to stand. Milk, margarine, mayonnaise and salad cream are common examples of emulsions. See **emulsifier**.

English mustard A bright yellow mustard with a straightforward hot taste. English mustard is made of blended seeds which have been finely ground and sifted and mixed with flour and spices, but no wine or vinegar. English mustard is available both in powder form to be mixed with water, or in a ready-to-use form. It is the traditional accompaniment to roast beef, ham, meat pies and sausages.

E number The E prefix is a standard identification code allocated to a food additive by the European Commission. It means that the additive is permitted for use in all member states. An additive number without an E prefix indicates that the additive is on a permitted list, but only in an individual country or in several of the member states.

According to the Food Labelling Regulations (1984) additives in food for sale in the UK must be listed on the label, either by the chemical name (e.g. butylated hydroxytoluene) or by the E number and category (e.g. antioxidant E321). In this book, additives are listed under their chemical names, with the E number following in brackets. There is a complete list of additives' E numbers and numbers, with their corresponding chemical names, at the end of the book. See also **unnumbered additive**.

enzyme A **protein** that acts as a catalyst, it causes or accelerates a biochemical reaction without itself being used up in the process. Their names generally end in *-ase* and each reaction has its own specific enzyme, e.g. the enzyme lactase catalyses the breakdown of the milk sugar lactose. Enzymes are the principal constituents of digestive juices. They occur in many foods and fulfil various purposes. The enzymes in cereals control the conversion of starch to sugars (as in the malting of barley). The muscle fibres of meat that is left to hang are broken down by enzymes, making the meat more tender. See also **tenderizers**.

Epsom salts Alternative name for **magnesium sulphate**.

erythrosine (E127) A synthetic **coal tar dye** employed to colour foods pink or red. It may also be used with other blue **colouring** agents to produce purple or violet shades. It was formerly used widely, but because it contains **iodine**, which in excess could affect the thyroid gland (especially in children), the **COT** has recommended that its use be limited to cocktail cherries and glacé cherries to a specified maximum content. Erythrosine is banned in Japan and Norway.

ester A compound formed when an **acid** reacts with an **alcohol**. Many esters occur naturally in foods, to which they contribute flavour and aroma. Chemically, most fats and oils are **glycerol** esters of fatty acids. Some esters are used as food additives. Others can find their way into food – for instance, esters are employed to make plastics more pliable and

99

they may leach out into food stored in plastic containers.

ethanol Alternative name for **ethyl alcohol**.

ethanolamine Alternative name for **2-aminoethanol**.

ether Alternative name for **diethyl ether**.

ethoxyquin An **antioxidant** added to animal feedstuffs, but only used in foods for human consumption to treat the surface of apples and pears. It cannot be used in foods for babies and young children.

ethyl acetate (also called **ethyl ethanoate**) An organic **solvent** used to **decaffeinate** coffee.

ethyl alcohol (also called **ethanol**) The **alcohol** in **alcoholic drinks**, formed in the making of beer, cider and wine by the fermentation of various sugars. It can also be made synthetically. In the food industry it is used as a **solvent**.

ethyl ester of beta-apo–8′-carotenoic acid (**E160f**; also called **ethyl ester of capsanthin**) A synthetic **colouring** agent employed to dye foods (e.g. butter oil) yellow or orange.

ethyl 4-hydroxybenzoate (E214; also called **ethyl para-hydroxybenzene)** A synthetic **preservative** made from **benzoic acid**, used to prevent the growth of or to kill bacteria and fungi in a wide range of foods from beer and coffee essence to fruit products and marinated fish. People who have **asthma, aspirin sensitivity** or **urticaria** may also have a sensitivity to this benzoate, which has also been found to cause **contact dermatitis** in a few people. It is not recommended for children with a history of **hyperactivity**. The same remarks apply to its sodium salt.

ethyl 4-hydroxybenzoate, sodium salt (E215; also called **sodium ethyl para-hydroxybenzoate)** An antibacterial and antifungal **preservative** made from **benzoic acid**. See **ethyl 4-hydroxybenzoate**.

ethyl maltol (637) A synthetic sweet-tasting **flavouring** and **flavour enhancer** made from the plant product **maltol**. It is found in bread, cakes, chocolate drinks, ice cream and soft drinks. It is not permitted in foods for babies and young children.

ethylmethylcellulose (E465; also called **methylethylcellulose)** A synthetic derivative of cellulose employed as an **emulsifier, stabilizer** and **thickener**. It can be found in bottled sauces and whipped toppings.

ethyl para-hydroxybenzoate Alternative name for **ethyl 4-hydroxybenzoate**.

excipient An inert substance employed as a 'carrier' for an additive used in bread-making. The name derives from the medical use of the term for an inactive carrier of an active substance, usually a drug, in a solid or liquid medicine.

extender A substance used in meat products to make the meat content go further. Extenders are often based on **soya bean** products, such as **textured vegetable protein**. Most extenders cannot be used to replace the minimum meat content required by law in meat products. The use of meat extenders must be declared on the label.

extracts of natural origin rich in tocopherols (**E306**; also called **vitamin E**) An **antioxidant** and unstable form of **vitamin E** extracted by vacuum distillation from substances rich in the vitamin, including cottonseed, soya bean oil and wheat germ. It is employed in foods that contain polyunsaturated fats and for preventing the oxidation of vitamin A. It does not tolerate freezing. It is found in meat pies and vegetable oils.

extract of quillaia (also called **quillaia**) A **foaming agent** and **flavouring** made from the inner bark of the quillaia tree or soapbark, a tree of the rose family that grows in South America. It is used in some ice creams, soft drinks and sweets.

extrusion cooking A commercial cooking process that involves forcing food, in a plastic or paste state, through variously shaped apertures to give the finished product a particular shape. The extruded product is usually cooked immediately by 'flash-frying'. The process is used to make snack foods (particularly breakfast cereals), pasta and soya bean products.

FAC Abbreviation of **Food Advisory Committee**.

factory farming (also called **intensive farming**) A method of rearing food animals indoors using modern industrial methods, often with animals caged or penned in a small space. Chickens, pigs and calves are the animals most commonly reared in this way, because it produces large quantities of food efficiently and cheaply.

fats Large organic compounds that are insoluble in water and are found in the body as fat, and as a nutrient in food. They are made up of **triglycerides**, compounds of **glycerol** and fatty acids. Foods with a high fat content include vegetable oils, dripping, lard, butter, margarine, cream, nuts and some meats. See also **oil**.

Feingold diet The diet advised by the US allergy specialist Dr Ben Feingold for **hyperactive** children. It requires the removal of all **artificial colour** and **flavouring**, **glutamates**, **nitrates and nitrites**, **BHA** and **BHT** and **benzoic acid** from the diet. For the first four weeks of the diet, natural **salicylates** or aspirin-like substances are also avoided and then introduced gradually, one at a time. The Feingold diet is not popular with all members of the medical profession, but many parents have found it helpful in treating their hyperactive children.

fennel An aromatic umbelliferous plant whose leaves and seeds have a slightly aniseed flavour, used to flavour food, particularly fish.

fennel seed The seeds of the **fennel** plant, used as a savoury flavouring, particularly in fish dishes.

fenugreek An aromatic leguminous plant that grows in Mediterranean regions, whose seeds are ground to a powder and used as a spice.

ferric ammonium citrate Alternative name for **ammonium ferric citrate**.

fines herbes   A culinary term for a mixture of finely chopped herbs, usually chive, chervil, parsley and tarragon, although other herbs may be used. Fines herbes are traditionally used in omelettes and with fish and poultry.

firming agent   A food additive often included with processed or preserved fruits and vegetables to retain their natural crispness. It is used particularly in canned products because **canning** tends to soften the food. Most firming agents are aluminium, calcium or magnesium salts.

fish   Any of a large group of edible aquatic vertebrates found in both the sea and fresh water. Fish is highly perishable and the majority is bought as canned, frozen or smoked fish. Fish feed may contain added **preservatives** and **colourings** which can be carried over into the fish. The pink colour of salmon and trout flesh can often be attributed to the use of additives. See also **canned fish**; **frozen fish**; **smoked fish**.

fish fingers   Fish, usually cod, that is coated in batter (water, flour and oil) and breadcrumbs, and then frozen. At present, the content of fish fingers is not controlled, but regulations are being considered to impose a standard amount. **Polyphosphates** (E450) are used in many varieties to help increase the amount of added water retained in the product. In effect this reduces the amount of fish and increases the amount of water that the shopper is buying. The breadcrumb coating may contain added colour, possibly **tartrazine**. **Emulsifiers** and **flavour enhancers** may also be added. Brands are available that do not contain any artificial additives and some that use wholemeal breadcrumbs.

fish paste and spread   A savoury spread for bread and biscuits made predominantly of fish, with a variety of other ingredients, including water, oil and rusk. The amount of fish in fish pastes and spreads is controlled by law, both the minimum amount of total fish and the amount of the fish that gives its name to the product. A variety of additives may be found in such products including **preservatives, antioxidants, colouring, stabilizers, emulsifiers, flavourings** and other miscellaneous additives. Some brands are available that are free from artificial additives.

fish product   Any edible product made predominantly from fish, which is either ready-to-eat or requires further cooking after purchase. The composition of such products is not controlled by specific regulations except in the case of fish cakes and **fish pastes and spreads**. Fish cakes must contain a minimum of 35% fish. A variety of additives may be used in fish products, including **preservatives**, **antioxidants**, **colouring**, **stabilizers**, **emulsifiers**, **flavourings** and other miscellaneous additives such as **sequestrants**.

flatulence The uncomfortable presence of air or other gas in the stomach or intestines, caused by swallowing air during hasty eating, ingestion of gaseous foods (e.g. some beers and fizzy drinks) or eating foods that generate gases during digestion, perhaps by fermentation. It is often a symptom that accompanies indigestion. Certain foods, such as baked beans and Brussels sprouts, have a reputation for causing flatulence. So do fibrous or starchy food additives such as **agar** and **tragacanth**.

flavour A formal term in labelling which often follows the name of a familiar food, e.g. 'cheese flavour' or 'raspberry flavour'. This description means that the taste is created by including an additive, possibly a synthetic substance, that imitates a particular flavour. However, the products need contain no real cheese or raspberries. Flavour is also used loosely to mean any flavouring, natural or artificial. See **artificial flavour**; **flavoured**.

flavoured A term in food labelling that indicates that the product contains some of the named (natural) substance that contributes to the flavour. Thus 'cheese-flavoured crisps' or 'raspberry-flavoured yoghurt' do have to contain some cheese or raspberries. See also **flavour**.

flavour enhancer A food additive that stimulates the taste buds and 'brings out' the flavour of the food, making it tastier. It may restore some of the flavour lost in processing, but does not add any flavour of its own. The best-known flavour enhancers are the traditional substance **salt**, and **monosodium glutamate** (MSG), which has been associated with an unfavourable reaction, **Chinese restaurant syndrome**, in some susceptible people. Additional flavour enhancers include other glutamates, **maltol** and **sodium 5'-inosinate**.

flavoured vinegar Any vinegar that has ingredients added to give it more subtle flavours. Herbs such as **tarragon**, **garlic** or fruit such as crushed raspberries may be used. Flavoured vinegars still conform to the legal requirement of 4% acidity.

flavouring A substance added to food to give it a particular taste. It may be natural or artificial, or a synthetic copy of a natural substance, termed 'nature-identical'. However, as long as it is not specified, e.g. 'cheese flavouring' or 'strawberry flavouring', it may be listed on a label merely as 'flavouring'. If there are 2 or 20 such additives, they need only be declared simply as 'flavourings', without specifying how many there are. See also **flavour**; **flavoured**.

flavour modifier A food additive that reduces the taste of a food, without itself contributing to it.

flavoxanthin (E161a) A natural **xanthophyll** plant pigment, used to impart a yellow colour to foods.

flour A powder, which may be either fine or coarse, made when a cereal (usually wheat) is sifted and ground. It is used particularly for bread-making and baking.

Strong flour, which is rich in **gluten**, is employed for bread-making. Weak flour, low in gluten, is used to make biscuits, cakes and pasta. Wholemeal flour contains the ground-up fibrous husks of the wheat (bran). White flour, which does not contain the outer layers of the grain (bran and germ), must by law contain added **iron**, vitamin B$_1$ or **thiamin** and **niacin**. By law, all flours with the exception of wholemeal flour must also contain added **calcium**. These nutrient additions do not have to be declared in the ingredient list on the package.

Wholemeal flour is permitted to contain added colour as **caramel**. Many additives are permitted in other flours, but these tend to be added only to the flour used by manufacturers. These additives include **preservatives**, **emulsifiers**, **raising agents**, **bleaches** and **improvers**. Any additives such as raising agents added to shop-bought flour must be declared on the label. Flour was originally ground between stones, and flour milled in this way today is labelled 'stoneground' on the packet.

flour treatment agent A group of substances employed in the production of flour, including **bleaching agents** (such as **chlorine** and **chlorine dioxide**) and **stearyl tartrate**. **Potassium bromate**, formerly used for this purpose, has recently been banned in the UK. See also **improving agent**.

fluorine A highly reactive poisonous yellowish gas that occurs only in its chemical compounds, chief of which are fluorides. In areas where fluoride does not occur naturally in the drinking water, it is sometimes added (fluoridation) because it has been shown that traces of fluoride greatly reduce the incidence of tooth decay in children. Fluorides are also added to toothpaste for this purpose.

foam stabilizer A substance added to foods to prevent a froth or foam (such as the 'head' on lager) from collapsing. Foam stabilizers are also used in cottage cheese, gateaux and whipped toppings. They include **ethylmethylcellulose** and **extract of quillaia**. See also **stabilizer**.

folic acid (also called **folacin; pteroyl-L-glutamic acid**) One of the B vitamins, found in green vegetables, kidney, liver, mushrooms and yeast. It is necessary for the growth of red blood cells, and a deficiency of folic acid results in **anaemia**. See also **vitamin B complex**.

Food Advisory Committee (FAC) An organization that advises the Ministry of Agriculture, Fisheries and Food. It deals with matters relating to the composition, labelling and advertising of food, and on additives, contaminants and other substances which may be present in food or used in its preparation. It also reports to the Secretary of State for Health. In doing so, the Committee is implementing the **Food Act (1984)**. It is helped in its work by various other groups, such as the Department of Health's **Committee on the Toxicity of Chemicals in Food** (COT) and the **Committee on Medical Aspects of Food** (COMA).

Food Act (1984) The main legislation that controls the composition, production and marketing of food in the UK, including the use of additives. Regulations concerning additives, signed by ministers in the Ministry of Agriculture, Fisheries and Food based on reports from the **Food Advisory Committee**, become law as part of this Act.

food allergy An allergic reaction caused by eating certain foods. Such reactions are difficult to assess because not all people are affected by a particular food, and those who are are not necessarily all affected in the same way.

Basically, if somebody's immune system recognizes a component of food as an **allergen**, it responds by defending itself against the allergen. Often this involves the formation of **antibodies** and the release of **histamine** into the tissues, an action that can cause various symptoms, including running eyes and nose with laboured breathing (like **asthma** or **hay fever**), swelling and weals on the skin (**angioedema** and **urticaria**), skin eruptions (**eczema**) and, in children, **hyperactivity**. Stomach and **bowel problems**, with nausea, stomach cramps, vomiting and **diarrhoea**, are also common symptoms. In its most extreme and dangerous form, a food allergy may cause **anaphylaxis**. Antihistamines may be prescribed for short-term treatment of an allergy, but in the long-term the only sensible course is to identify the food or additive that causes the trouble and to avoid it.

Food and Drugs Act (1955) The Act of Parliament that forms the basis of current legislation for the control of the use of additives in food. It has now been consolidated into the **Food Act (1984)**.

food aversion A psychological avoidance and intolerance of food. An intolerance to foods involves emotions associated with the food rather than the food itself. These emotions cause an unpleasant reaction in the body, but, unlike a **food allergy**, there is no reaction when the food is given in an unrecognizable form. An aversion to all foods is a symptom of anorexia nervosa, a severe personality disorder that usually requires psychotherapy. See also **food intolerance**.

food black Alternative name for **black PN**.

food brown Alternative name for **brown FK**.

food-grade mineral oils Alternative name for **mineral hydrocarbons**.

food green S Alternative name for **green S**.

food intolerance An unpleasant reaction to a specific food or ingredient which is not psychologically based. Food intolerance occurs even when the affected person cannot identify the food. Examples of intolerance include enzyme defects, e.g. lactose intolerance (the inability to digest lactose due to a lack of the enzyme lactase), pharmacological effects, e.g. excessive intakes of caffeine, irritant effects and allergic reactions, as well as other mechanisms not yet identified.

food irradiation   A method of sterilizing food using ionizing radiation, usually X-rays or gamma-rays. It kills all microorganisms in food, including those that cause diseases in people or which make the food go bad.

Food irradiation affects the nutritional content of food less than other methods of preservation. But the method has aroused controversy because it is theoretically possible to apply it to food that is already 'off' (and containing toxins that are unaffected by irradiation) and then offer the food for sale. It is not possible to tell whether food has been irradiated just by looking at it. See also INTRODUCTION, PAGE V.

Food Labelling Regulations (1984)   The legal requirements concerning the labelling of food in the UK. They state that pre-packed foods have to carry certain information on their labels, such as the name of the food in straightforward terms, its weight, volume or the number of items in the pack, what it is made from (including any additives, which must have their additive category and chemical names or their **E numbers**) and often a **best before date** or **sell by date**. The ingredients must be listed in descending order of weight. There are certain exceptions, such as most **alcoholic drinks** and foods sold loose or unwrapped.

The form of the food and any special storage requirements must also be given, such as 'powdered food, store in a cool or dry place'. The name and address of the manufacturer must be stated, and many food labels also carry codes that tell the producer the date of manufacture (this is not a legal requirement). In addition many manufacturers voluntarily provide nutritional information and some may also claim particular benefits from a food. Increasingly there is a bar code that identifies the product and works the till at the supermarket checkout.

food preservation Any of various methods of preserving food, from traditional ones such as bottling, curing, drying, pickling, salting and smoking, to modern developments such as **canning**, **dehydration**, **food irradiation**, **freeze drying** and **freezing**. Chemical **preservatives** may also be added directly to a food.

food yellow 5 Alternative name for **yellow 2G**.

formic acid (E236; also called **methanoic acid)** An organic **acid** that occurs naturally in nettles and ants' venom, but which is made synthetically for use as a **flavouring** and **preservative**. It is banned completely in the UK and as a preservative in the US.

free radical A highly reactive chemical species which has been associated with the development of cancer in experimental animals. Organic free radicals may be formed when food is burned, and for this reason some experts advise against overindulgence in dishes that have been barbecued, charred or toasted.

freezant A substance that is applied directly to food to chill or freeze it, as opposed to normal **freezing** by refrigeration. Freezants include liquid **carbon dioxide**, liquid **nitrogen** and **dichlorodifluoromethane** (Freon–12), used in the process known as cryogenic freezing.

freeze drying A method of preserving food by freezing it and drying it. The food is first rapidly frozen, and then the water removed by subjecting it to very low pressure (vacuum). It is thus an alternative method of **dehydration**, used particularly for soups and instant beverages.

The method has several advantages: the vitamin content of food is affected less than other methods of preservation; freeze dried foods are more compact than frozen ones; and unlike frozen foods, freeze dried foods do not have to be kept refrigerated.

freezing A method of preserving that retains the nutritional value and flavour of food better than most other methods. The secret of achieving this aim is to freeze the food rapidly and while it is still fresh – immediately after it is caught, cooked, killed or picked. Peas, for example, are washed, graded and frozen within minutes of being picked. Fish is gutted and if necessary filleted and then frozen on board processing ships within an hour of being caught. Frozen food will keep indefinitely if stored in a freezer at below –18°C. See also **freeze drying**.

French chalk Alternative name for **talc**.

frozen fish Any fish that has been frozen to preserve it and to increase the shelf life of an otherwise highly perishable but nutritious food. Frozen fish is usually glazed with ice to prevent breakdown of **protein**. A Code of Practice permits the addition of up to 15% of the total weight as water. This should be borne in mind when buying a particular weight of fish for a recipe. Frozen fish may also contain **polyphosphates** (E450), which help to increase the amount of water retained. See also **freezing**.

frozen food A food that has been frozen to preserve it, increase the shelf life and make seasonal foods available all the year round. The loss of nutrients during freezing is small, although care must be taken to retain the nutrient content by reading and following the manufacturer's instructions for thawing and cooking.

Single frozen food items, such as fruit and vegetables, are unlikely to contain added ingredients such as sugar, salt or additives. Frozen dishes, such as those in sauce and frozen meals, may contain additives, and the ingredients list should be checked carefully.

fructose A sugar that is found in ripe fruits and honey, and combined with **glucose** forms **sucrose**. It is similar to glucose but twice as sweet.

fruit The fleshy, ripened ovary of a plant, containing one or more seeds. Fresh fruit is a good source of fibre and vitamins, supplying energy in the form of **carbohydrates** without being excessively high in calories. However, not all of these qualities remain after fruit has been stored, cooked, processed or preserved.

Overcooking (particularly boiling) and **canning**, for example, can affect the colour, crispness, flavour and vitamin content of fruits, some of which can be restored by various additives, e.g. **artificial colours**, **firming agents**, **artificial flavours**, **vitamins** and **flavour enhancers**.

Other methods of preservation such as **freezing** do less damage. Even in store, before it is processed or sold, fruit can deteriorate because it can continue to ripen and is susceptible to attack by moulds. Picking fruit while it is still unripe and then controlling its ripening with ethylene (ethene) gas overcomes the first problem. Treating the fruit with a fungicide, or wrapping it in paper impregnated with one, overcomes the second. See also **dried fruit**.

fruit crush A ready-to-drink product that must by law contain 5% fruit juice. Fruit crush may be sweetened with a specified minimum amount of sugar, or an **artificial sweetener** such as **saccharin** may be used.

fruit juice A juice extracted from fruit, which may be sold as 'pure juice' or 'fruit juice'. Fruit juice may be sold as juice squeezed from the fruit with no pith or peel, as concentrated fruit juice that has been reduced by at least 50% by evaporation of the water, and as reconstituted juice made from concentrated fruit juice.

Sugar may be added up to a level of 15 g per litre without a declaration on the pack, but if more than this is used the product must be labelled 'sweetened'. Sweetening may be in the form of **glucose**, **fructose** or syrups. Acids, added vitamin C, **flavourings** and **preservatives** are permitted in all fruit juices and pineapple

119

juice may also contain the **anti-foaming agent dimethylpolysiloxane**. Orange juice is permitted to contain up to 10 mg per litre of **sulphur dioxide** without a declaration on the list of ingredients. This level is extremely low compared with levels found in other foods.

fruit nectar A ready-to-drink product made of fruit juice, sugar and water. Fruit juice is present in amounts between 25% and 50%. Fruit nectars may contain acids, **colourings**, **emulsifiers**, **flavouring** and other miscellaneous additives.

fruit squash A concentrated fruit drink that requires dilution before it is consumed. Citrus fruit squashes must by law contain 25% fruit juice and non-citrus fruit squashes 10% fruit juice. Some squashes contain more fruit juice than these legal minimums and are labelled 'high juice'. Fruit squashes are sweetened with a specified minimum amount of sugar, or an **artificial sweetener** such as **saccharin** may be used.

Fruit squashes may contain several additives, including **preservatives**, **colourings**, **flavourings**, **emulsifiers**, **stabilizers**, **acidity regulators**, acids and **artificial sweeteners**. Although **tartrazine** has been removed from many brands, fruit squashes still continue to contain a large number of additives and a high level of sugar.

fuller's earth A clay mineral originally used for 'fulling' – removing the grease – from wool. It is now employed in the food industry to decolorize fats and oils and as a **release agent**.

fumaric acid (297) An organic **acid** that is employed as an **acidity regulator** and flavouring; it is also used as a **raising agent** in baked goods. It is found in some cheesecake mixes, desserts, jams and jellies, and sweets.

furcellaran (E408) A **gelling agent, thickening agent** and **stabilizer** extracted from seaweeds along with **carrageenan**. It is used in various milk-based foods and drinks, cheeses, meat pies, jams and jellies.

gamma-carotene (E160a) An orange-yellow **colouring** agent that occurs naturally in carrots, oranges and tomatoes but is mainly made synthetically. Its properties and uses are the same as those of **alpha-carotene**.

gamma-tocopherol, synthetic (E308; also called **vitamin E)** A synthetic form of vitamin E, employed as a vitamin supplement. It is used as a vitamin supplement in flour, margarine and white bread, and as an **antioxidant** in meat pies and sausages. See also **alpha-tocopherol, synthetic**.

garlic The pungent aromatic bulb (consisting of several segments, or cloves) of a plant of the onion family, used to add a characteristic flavour to savoury dishes often associated with French and Italian cuisine. It is available fresh, shredded and dried (as garlic granules) or as an oil-based essence. Garlic salt is made by mixing dried, pounded garlic with refined salt crystals, and is used as a seasoning in a variety of savoury dishes. The chemicals that give garlic its flavour linger on the breath and may be excreted through the skin in sweat.

gastric upset Most stomach disorders related to food result from overeating or over-ambitious use of hot spices or sauces. The next most common cause is contaminated food, whose most extreme manifestation is food poisoning.

There are some foods that cause gastric upsets in susceptible people, usually because of a **food aversion** or **food intolerance** of the food. The same may be said for certain food additives. Most notorious in this context are **colouring** agents, particularly **azo dyes** and **coal tar dyes** (associated with **hyperactivity** in some children), **antioxidants** and **preservatives**. See also **bowel problems**.

gelatin (also called **gelatine**) A natural but indigestible **protein** made commercially from animal and fish residues (such as bones, hides and horns). It is used as a glue and adhesive, and in the food industry as a **gelling agent** and **thickener**, because it swells in contact with water. Some sweets, such as fruit gums, may be made almost entirely of gelatin. One pure form of the additive is called **isinglass**. Gelatin is not suitable for vegetarians, but alternative gelling agents and thickeners include **agar** and **carrageenan**.

gelling agent A substance that thickens a food or helps it to set, forming a jelly. Gelling agents are used in fruit fillings, jams, meat products, soups, sweets and, of course, jellies. They include **agar**, **alginates** and **carrageenan** (all made from seaweed), **gelatin** (made from animal residues) and various vegetable gums.

German mustard A mustard made from strong mustard flour and vinegar. It is not as hot as English mustard and is a popular accompaniment to German sausage and frankfurters.

ginger A spicy, pungent condiment and flavouring made from the dried underground stems of the ginger plant, which is native to eastern Asia but cultivated throughout the tropics. Root ginger is available fresh or dried, or in a dried ground, powder form. The undried stems (stem ginger) may also be candied and used as a dessert.

glacé cherry A cherry preserved in a heavy syrup usually of **sugar** and **glucose**. Glacé cherries may contain **preservatives** and **artificial colour**, although some brands are available that contain natural colour.

Glauber's salt   Alternative name for sodium sulphate.

glazing agent   A substance that is used to coat food, such as pies and sweets, to give them a glassy, polished appearance. Most glazing agents are waxes, and they may also serve to protect the food they are applied to.

glucono delta-lactone   Alternative name for **D-glucono-1,5-lactone**.

D-glucono-1,5-lactone (575; also called **glucono delta-lactone)**   An acidic substance made from **glucose** and used as a **raising agent** and **sequestrant**. It is employed to prevent the precipitation of insoluble phosphates during the production of beer and milk products. It may be found in baking powders, cake mixes, jelly powders and soft drink mixes.

glucose   (also   called   **dextrose**;   **grape sugar**)   A sweet-tasting substance, chemically a type of **monosaccharide** sugar, that occurs in many plants. It is the basic carbohydrate building-block of cellulose and starch, from which it can be made by hydrolysis using acids or the action of **enzymes**. **Sucrose** is a combination of glucose and **fructose**.

In the human body glucose is the end product of the digestion of carbohydrates, and is used as a source of metabolic energy. It is the sugar present in the blood, in which its level is controlled by the hormone insulin (see **diabetes**). Glucose is about half as sweet as cane-sugar, and it is a common ingredient of many manufactured foods.

glucose syrup A sweet liquid consisting of a mixture of **glucose** and other sugars. It is used in the food industry as an alternative to sugar.

L-glutamic acid (620; also called alphaaminoglutaric acid) An **amino acid** made by the hydrolysis of the vegetable protein in wheat **gluten** or molasses, or by the bacterial fermentation of carbohydrates in the presence of ammonium salts. It is employed as a **flavour enhancer** and salt-like condiment in meat pies, packet sauces and soups, sausages and various savoury snacks. Like its sodium salt, **monosodium glutamate** (MSG), L-glutamic acid may cause an allergic reaction in some susceptible people. See **Chinese restaurant syndrome**.

gluten A **protein** present in the cereals wheat and rye, and to a lesser extent oats, whose concentration determines the 'strength' of the **flour** made from the wheat ('strong' flour is used for making bread). A **food intolerance** to gluten gives rise to **coeliac disease**.

gluten bread   A type of bread made from 'strong' **flour** that contains a high percentage of **gluten** and a minimum of 16% protein.

glycerin(e)   Alternative name for **glycerol**.

glycerol (E422; also called **glycerin**; **glycerine)**   An organic liquid, chemically resembling both an **alcohol** and a **sugar**, with a sweetish hot taste. It is about half as sweet as sugar. It occurs naturally in plants, but is obtained commercially as a by-product of soap manufacture – the fats and oils used in the process are **glycerol** esters of fatty acids. It may also be synthesized from propene (propylene) or made by fermenting various sugars. It is used as a **humectant**, **solvent** (for other additives) and **sweetener**, and as a plasticizer in skins for sausages and cheese. It is also found in baked goods, beverages, fudge and icing, and in chewing gum, marshmallow and other sweets.

glycerol diacetate (also called **diacetin**)   A **solvent** and carrier for other food additives, such as **flavourings**.

glycerol monoacetate   A **solvent** and carrier for other food additives, such as **flavourings**, used in combination with **glycerol**.

glycerol triacetate (also called **triacetin**)   A **humectant**, **solvent** and carrier for other food additives, such as **flavourings**.

glyceryl monostearate; glyceryl distearate Alternative names for **mono-** and **diglycerides of fatty acids**.

glycine (also called **aminoacetic acid**; **aminoethanoic acid**) The simplest **amino acid**, released from food in the body by the digestion of proteins; it can be manufactured from animal protein. It is sometimes added to soft drinks that have been sweetened with **saccharin** to mask the sweetener's bitter aftertaste.

gold (E175) A precious yellow metal, employed to give a surface colour to dragées and other cake decorations.

granary bread A brown **bread** that has had malted flour added. Malted flour is wheat flour and malted wheat grains. Granary bread may contain **preservatives** and other additives permitted in bread other than wholemeal bread.

granary flour A brown **flour** that has had malted wheat grains added. See also **granary bread**.

grape sugar Alternative name for **glucose**.

green peppercorn The unripe berries of the East Indian pepper plant, used dried or pickled in brine as a condiment and seasoning.

green S (E142; also called acid **brilliant green**; **food green S; lissamine green**) A synthetic

coal tar dye, employed to impart a green colour to foods. It is very widely used in such foods as canned peas, cider, fruit fillings, jams, ice cream, lime drinks, mint sauce, packet breadcrumbs and soups. It is banned in Norway, Sweden and the US.

guanosine 5'-disodium phosphate (627; also called **sodium guanylate**)   A **flavour enhancer** that occurs naturally in sardines and yeast, from which it is extracted for use in the food industry. It is used in cured meats, gravy powders, potato snacks, pre-cooked savoury rice and soups. It is not recommended for people who suffer from gout and is not permitted in foods intended for babies or children. It is banned in the US.

guar gum (E412; also called **cluster bean**; **guar flour**; **jaguar gum**)   A **thickening agent** and **stabilizer**, employed also as a bulking agent. It is extracted from the seeds of a tropical Indian leguminous plant, which has also been introduced into the US. It is used in baked goods, bottled sauces, cream cheese, fruit drinks, ice cream, milk drinks, pickles, salad dressings, soups and syrups. Guar gum has been shown to aid **diabetics** to keep their blood glucose levels under control. Excessive amounts can cause flatulence and impair the absorption of trace elements in the intestines.

guar flour Alternative name for **guar gum**.

gum arabic (E414; also called **gum acacia; Sudan gum)** A natural gum obtained from the trunk and branches of an acacia tree that grows in northern and central Africa, the Middle East and India. It is employed as an **emulsifier, thickening agent** and **stabilizer** (to maintain the head on beer and fizzy drinks). It can be found in some cake mixes, canned vegetables, chewing gum, fruit gums and jellies.

gum dragon Alternative name for **tragacantha**.

gum tragacanth Alternative name for **tragacanth**.

gypsum Alternative name for **calcium sulphate**.

haemoglobin The red pigment in blood, consisting of a complex protein containing **iron**. See **anaemia**.

hay fever An allergic reaction to the inhalation of pollen and other airborne **allergens**. Its symptoms resemble those of a cold: running eyes and nose, sneezing and wheezing; there may also be a rash. These symptoms, probably prompted by the defensive release of **histamines**, are also characteristic of certain kinds of

food allergy. People who suffer from hay fever and other allergies should avoid certain food additives that may bring on similar symptoms.

health drink A term used to describe some brands of fruit squash or crush. They contain added vitamin C and sometimes other vitamins, but have a high sugar and additives content, making the description of 'health drink' questionable.

1,4-heptonolactone (370) A synthetic acidic organic compound employed as a **sequestrant**. It is used in some instant desserts and soups.

herb Part of an aromatic plant, usually the leaves, that is used fresh or dried, whole or ground to add flavour to food. Sometimes flower buds, flowers and seeds are also used as herbs. The use of seeds clouds the difference between herbs and **spices**, which generally have a more pungent flavour.

hexamine (E239; also called **hexamethylenetetramine**; **HMT**; **methenamine)** A synthetic organic compound, made from formaldehyde (methanal) and ammonia, once manufactured in large quantities as a high explosive for torpedoes. Today it is employed as a **preservative** for killing microbes in foods such as marinated fish (herring and mackerel) and soft provolone cheeses. It is banned in the US.

hexamethylene tetramine Alternative name for **hexamine**.

hexanedioic acid Alternative name for **adipic acid**.

high-fibre bread A **bread** made from white flour that has fibre added to it. The fibre may be in the form of **bran**, but other sources of fibre, such as peas or soya, may be used. High-fibre bread may contain **preservatives** and other additives permitted in bread other than wholemeal bread.

high-protein bread A **bread** that has a minimum protein content of 22%. High-protein bread may contain **preservatives** and other additives permitted in bread other than wholemeal bread.

histamine A substance produced by body tissues as a defensive mechanism against injury or the presence of an **allergen**. It is largely responsible for allergic reactions, including the symptoms of **asthma**, **hay fever**, **urticaria** and a **food allergy**. In large quantities, it may cause **anaphylaxis**. The natural presence of histamine in certain foods, such as chocolate, egg white, fish and strawberries, may be responsible for **food intolerance** in susceptible people.

HMT Abbreviation of hexamethylenetetramine, an alternative name for **hexamine**.

honey A sweet substance of variable composition, containing up to 80% of **invert sugar**, produced by bees from nectar. Its consistency may vary from a yellow sugary solid to a rich brown syrup, and its flavour depends to a large extent on the type of flowers visited by the bees. It is used as a sugar substitute, although it is much more expensive.

horseradish A pungent condiment made from the roots of a Eurasian plant of the mustard family. The root may be grated and pickled in vinegar, or blended with mayonnaise to make horseradish sauce. Traditionally it is served with roast beef, but it is also a popular accompaniment to smoked mackerel.

humectant A substance added to foods such as fondant icing, chocolates, jelly sweets and marshmallow to prevent them drying out and becoming hard. Humectants act by absorbing water from the air, and they include **glycerol**, **mannitol** and **sorbitol**.

hydrochloric acid (507) A mineral **acid** that occurs naturally in the stomach's digestive juices. It is employed commercially in the process for hydrolysing starch to make sugars and in a similar way in brewing to retain sugars during malting. It may also be used to adjust the acidity of the brewery's water supply if necessary, and may therefore be found in trace amounts in beer.

hydrogen A light, flammable gas employed in hydrogenation processes, such as the manufacture of margarine and cooking fat (which involves the hydrogenation of liquid oils to make them into solid fats). It is also used as the propellant in some aerosols and as a packaging gas.

hydrogenated glucose syrup A **sweetener** in which some of the **glucose** has been converted to **sorbitol**, made artificially by treating the substances formed in the hydrolysis of starch with hydrogen. It is nearly as sweet as ordinary sucrose but much cheaper, and often used in the food industry as a substitute for sucrose or glucose. It can have a slight laxative effect and is therefore not approved for foods intended for babies and young children.

hydrogenated isomaltitol Alternative name for **isomalt**.

hydrogenated vegetable oil A solid fat made by treating a liquid vegetable oil with hydrogen, e.g. most **margarines** and **cooking fats**. Hydrogenated fats have a higher saturated fatty acid content, and have longer shelf lives than other oils because they do not go rancid as quickly.

hydrogenation A chemical process that involves the addition of **hydrogen** to a substance, usually in the presence of a catalyst. It is used in the food industry as a method of converting liquid oils into solid fats.

hydrolysed vegetable protein A **protein** of vegetable origin that has been partly broken down into **amino acids**. Hydrolysed vegetable protein is used as a **flavouring** and **flavour enhancer** in savoury products, particularly those containing meat.

hydrolysis A chemical process that involves the interaction of a substance with water, usually in the presence of an **acid** or **alkali**, which acts as a catalyst.

2-hydroxybiphenyl (E231; also called **O-phenylphenol; orthophenylphenol; orthoxenol)** A **preservative** employed for preventing the growth of bacteria and fungi on the surfaces of citrus fruits. The fruit skins may be treated directly, or the substance may be incorporated in the paper in which the fruit is wrapped. It can get into marmalade and other cooked products that include fruit skins.

hydroxypropanoic acid Alternative name for **lactic acid**.

hydroxypropylcellulose (E463) An **emulsifier**, **stabilizer** and **thickener** made from cellulose and used in fruit pie fillings, whipped toppings and sweets.

hydroxypropylmethylcellulose (E464; also called **hypromellose)** An **emulsifier, gelling agent, stabilizer** and **thickener** made from cellulose. It is used in some baked products, ice creams, low-calorie dressings and potato products.

Hyperactive Children's Support Group A British charitable organization that helps hyperactive children and their parents. It has drawn up a list of food additives that have been associated with hyperactivity and which it recommends should be eliminated from the diets of such children. See **hyperactivity**.

hyperactivity A behavioural disorder in children that is characterized by excitability and restlessness, inattentiveness at school and a tendency to disturb the work of other children. A hyperactive child requires immediate attention and displays rapid swings of mood, from tears to bad-tempered outbursts. It is a difficult condition to diagnose, even for a doctor, who should be consulted if hyperactivity is suspected. Some authorities have associated the disorder with certain food additives, including **azo dyes** and **coal tar dyes** used as food **colouring** agents, and some **antioxidants** and **preservatives**. The **Hyperactive Children's Support Group** recommends that such additives should be eliminated from the diets of hyperactive children.

hypersensitivity An abnormal sensitivity to a substance that has little or no effect on most people, possibly because of a **food allergy** or **food intolerance**.

hypertension The medical term for high blood pressure. See **blood pressure problems**.

hypromellose Alternative name for **hydroxypropylmethylcellulose**.

ice cream A sweetened frozen dessert made from fat and sugar. Legally, ice cream must contain a minimum of 5% fat. In the case of **dairy ice cream** this must be milk fat, but non-dairy ice creams usually contain hardened vegetable oils, which themselves contain **antioxidants**. Ice cream also contains non-milk fat solids or skimmed milk. About half the weight of ice cream is water and half the volume is air. Additives to be found in ice cream include **colourings**, **flavourings** and **emulsifiers**.

ice lolly A sweetened frozen ice cream or water ice on a stick. An ice lolly may be a mixture of water, **sugar**, **colouring** and **flavouring**, but brands are now available that are based on fruit juice and which do not contain additives. Ice lollies may also contain **emulsifiers** and **stabilizers**.

immune response The body's reaction to the presence of invading 'foreign' substances, such as disease microorganisms (bacteria or viruses) or **allergens**. It includes the production of **antibodies** to combat the invaders. See also **food allergy**.

immunoglobulin A **protein** from which an **antibody** is made in the body as part of the **immune response**.

improving agent A substance added to **flour** so that bread dough made from it will tolerate a wide range of storage and baking conditions. Along with **bleaching agents**, improving agents are part of a wider category of additives sometimes collectively called **flour treatment agents**.

Indian tragacanth Alternative name for **karaya gum**.

indigo carmine (E132; also called **indigotine)** A **coal tar dye** used as a blue **colouring** agent in foods such as biscuits, powdered desserts, fruit fillings, soups and sweets. It is not recommended for people who suffer from allergies or for children with a history of **hyperactivity**.

indigotine Alternative name for **indigo carmine**.

infant food Alternative name for **baby food**.

Ingredient A component of a recipe, whether manufactured or home-made. All ingredients of manufactured foods, including additives, must be listed in descending order of weight. Water must be included if it is more that 5% of the weight of the finished product. See APPENDIX I, ADDITIVE-FREE SHOPPING.

ingredient labelling See **Food Labelling Regulations**.

ingredient list The constituents of a food that must be stated, if the food is pre-packed, in decreasing order of weight. See **Food Labelling Regulations**.

inosine 5′-(disodium phosphate) (631; also called **sodium 5′-inosinate)** A **flavour enhancer** made from meat and fish extracts. It is widely used in products such as potato crisps, cured meats and soups. It cannot be used in food intended for babies and young children and is not recommended for people who suffer from kidney disorders or gout.

inositol (also called **hexahydroxy-cyclohexane)** A sweet-tasting substance related to phytic acid found in many foods, particularly bran, cereals and yeast. It is often classified as one of the B complex vitamins and is made commercially from corn liquor.

instant coffee Coffee in the form of powder or granules made by **freeze drying**, which can be reconstituted by adding boiling water. It contains **caffeine**, but **decaffeinated** instant coffees are available. Instant coffees may also contain a **preservative** and an **emulsifier**.

instant pudding A manufactured sweet dish that is bought either ready to eat, or requires the minimum of preparation. Instant puddings include mousses, whips, creamy desserts, custards, trifles and cheesecakes. They tend to have high contents of sugar and fat, and may contain a variety of additives such as **colourings, flavourings, preservatives, antioxidants, emulsifiers, stabilizers** and **sweeteners**. There are healthier lower-fat and sugar alternatives available. See APPENDIX I, ADDITIVE-FREE SHOPPING.

instructions for use A set of instructions that must, by law, be given on labels if the food would be difficult to prepare without them. Any special cooking instructions must be given on products that would be spoilt if cooked in any other way, e.g. boil in the bag foods, which should not be cooked separately from the bag. Ingredients, other than water, that need to be added must also be clearly indicated. Special conditions of use must be shown, for instance some fat spreads are only suitable for spreading and should not be used for cooking.

intensive farming See **factory farming**.

intolerance See **food intolerance**.

invert sugar A mixture of **fructose** and **glucose** made (by acid **hydrolysis**) from cane-sugar, or **sucrose**. It is present in many ripe fruits and is the major constituent of honey. Invert sugar is easy to digest and is less sweet than cane-sugar. It is used extensively by food manufacturers.

iodine A purple-black, non-metallic element necessary in trace quantities in the diet for the proper functioning of the thyroid gland. Foods rich in iodine include fish, shellfish and some vegetables. Deficiency of iodine in the diet can lead to goitre, and for this reason iodine compounds are added to table salt in regions where the soil – and hence vegetables grown on it – lacks iodine.

iodized salt A table salt to which an **iodine** compound (usually potassium iodate) has been added to compensate for lack of this trace element in the diet.

Irish moss Alternative name for **carrageenan**.

irradiation of food See **food irradiation**.

iron A metallic element necessary in trace quantities in the diet for the manufacture of red blood cells. Foods rich in iron include liver, green leafy vegetables, peas and beans. Deficiency of iron in the diet can cause **anaemia**.

iron hydroxides (E172) Minerals used as **colouring** agents to impart yellow, red or brown colours to food. They are used in some fish and meat pastes, cake mixes and dessert mixes. They are banned in Germany, and in the US they may only be used in pet foods.

iron oxides (E172) Minerals with the same properties and uses as **iron hydroxides**.

isinglass A form of **gelatin** made from the swim bladders of fish, used as an adhesive, **gelling agent** and **thickener**, and to clarify beer and wine. The substance known as Japanese isinglass is in fact **agar**.

isomalt (also called **hydrogenated isomaltitol**; **isomaltitol**) A sweet-tasting substance used as a substitute for sugar in desserts, soft drinks and sweets. It is about half as sweet as sugar. It can have laxative effects and is not permitted in foods intended for babies and young children.

isopropyl alcohol (also called **isopropanol**; **2-propanol**) A type of alcohol used as a **solvent** for extracting substances from foods and to dissolve additives such as flavourings.

itching (also called **pruritis**) An annoying symptom of some skin disorders such as **eczema**, **contact dermatitis** and **urticaria**. It may thus have an allergic origin (see **food allergy**). It has been reported as a reaction to certain synthetic food **colouring** agents in some susceptible people.

jaguar gum Alternative name for **guar gum**.

jam A preserve made by boiling together sugar and fresh fruit until set. The high sugar content acts as a preservative and jam making is one of the traditional ways of preserving seasonal fresh fruit. The setting ability of any particular jam depends on the **pectin** content of the fruits. The difference between a jam and a conserve is that a jam contains fruit that has been crushed or pulped, while a conserve contains the whole fruit preserved in syrup.

Jams may contain a variety of additives including **sulphur dioxide** (already present in the fruit and therefore not declared), **preservatives**, **sweeteners**, **acidity regulators** and **gelling agents**. By law jams must contain 60% added sugar and in the majority of varieties at least 35% fruit. Reduced sugar jams must contain 30–55% added sugar. No-added sugar jams are usually sweetened with grape juice, or some other fruit juice. Many of these varieties are free from additives, but they have a shorter shelf life than traditional jams and once opened must be kept in the fridge. Extra jams still contain 60% added sugar, but have a higher fruit content. Fruit used in such products cannot be treated with sulphur dioxide.

Jamaican pepper Alternative name for **allspice**.

Japanese isinglass Alternative name for **agar**.

juniper berry The small purple berry of an evergreen tree or shrub that grows throughout the northern hemisphere. It has an aromatic flavour with a hint of pine, and is used fresh, dried or pickled in brine for flavouring food. Juniper is the principal flavouring agent in gin.

kaolin (559; also called **aluminium silicate; china clay)** A mineral used as an **anti-caking agent** in the powdered milk for vending machines and to clarify wine, in which it may also be found. It is banned in the US.

karaya gum (416; also called **Indian tragacanth; sterculia gum)** A natural gum that is obtained from the trunk of an Indian tree. It is used as an **emulsifier, stabilizer** and **thickener**. It can absorb up to 100 times its own volume of water and is therefore also used as a filler. It can be found in some baked goods, cheeses, ice cream, ice lollies, meat products, pickles, sauces and sweets. Karaya gum has been known to cause an allergic reaction in some sensitive people.

kidney problems Disorders of the kidneys have been associated with high intakes of some food additives. Inflammation of the kidneys (nephritis) has accompanied the ingestion of **potassium nitrate**, and kidney stones (renal calculi) may be caused by excess phosphates.

kipper brown Alternative name for **brown FK**.

labelling See **Food Labelling Regulations**.

Labelling of Food Regulations See **Food Labelling Regulations**.

lactic acid (E270; also called **DL-lactic acid**; **hydroxypropanoic acid**) A liquid organic **acid** that occurs naturally in sour milk, molasses and various fruits, but is made synthetically for the food industry by the fermentation of starchy substances (e.g. cornstarch, potatoes) or by the alkaline **hydrolysis** of **glucose**. It is employed as a flavouring agent, **preservative** and **synergist** for **antioxidants**. It may be used as an alternative to vinegar (or acetic acid) in making pickles. Lactic acid is also used in malting barley to retain the sugar content, and may be added to the water used in brewing to adjust the acidity of the local water supply. It is found in a wide range of foods and drinks, including beer, canned fruit and fish, fizzy drinks, jams and jellies, margarines, pickles and sauces, and salad dressings.

lactic acid esters of mono- and diglycerides of fatty acids (E472b; also called **lactoglycerides) Emulsifiers** and **stabilizers** made from **glycerol** and **lactic acid**, used in baked products, cooking fats, packet cake mixes and dessert toppings, and soups.

lactoflavin Alternative name for **riboflavin**.

lactoglycerides Alternative name for **lactic acid esters of mono- and diglycerides of fatty acids**.

lactose A sugar that occurs in milk (4.7% in cows' milk) that forms **lactic acid** when milk goes sour. It is sometimes used as a **sweetener**, but is less than half as sweet as **sucrose**.

lactylated fatty acid esters of glycerol and propane–1,2-diol (478) Emulsifiers and **stabilizers**, used also as plasticizers and whipping agents. They can be found in some baked goods and dessert mixes.

lager See **beer**.

lecithins (E322; also called phosphotids; phospholipids) Fat-related substances that occur in all living tissue, particularly eggs, cereals, milk, pulses and vegetable oils. For commercial use they are extracted from soya beans, and employed as **antioxidants** and **emulsifiers**. They can be found in baked goods, bread, breakfast cereals, chocolate, dessert mixes, ice cream, margarine, mayonnaise, milk powder and sweets.

lemon A citrus fruit, grown in many warm parts of the world, which is used mainly for its flavour in sweet and savoury dishes. Lemons are rich in **ascorbic acid** (vitamin C) and **citric acid**. They also contain **pectin**, which accounts for their use as an aid for the setting of jam made from fruits that are low in pectin. Lemon juice can be used to brush the cut surfaces of fresh fruit and vegetables to prevent discoloration.

lime Alternative name for **calcium oxide**.

liqueur An alcoholic drink distilled from wine or brandy. It contains between 30–40 g/100 ml alcohol and is sweetened and flavoured with sugar, fruit, herbs and spices. As with all drinks with an alcoholic strength by volume of more than 1.2%, liqueurs do not have to carry a list of ingredients on the label. A variety of additives may be used including **colouring**, **preservatives** and **processing aids**.

liquid freezant An extremely cold liquid, such as liquid **carbon dioxide** or liquid **nitrogen**, applied directly to foods to freeze them rapidly. See **freezant**; **freezing**.

lissamine green Alternative name for **green S**.

listeria (also called **listerellosis**) A disease caused by *Listeria monocytogenes* bacteria, which can infect cattle, sheep and poultry (particularly chickens and their eggs) and can pass from milk into milk products. Listeria may result in meningitis, and those most at risk from the disease include children, pregnant women and the elderly.

lithol rubine BK Alternative name for **pigment rubine**.

locust bean gum (E410; also called **carob bean gum**; **ceratonia gum**) A **gelling agent**, **stabilizer** and **thickener** extracted from the seeds of the carob or locust tree, an evergreen leguminous plant of the Mediterranean region. It is used in canned fish and vegetables, cheese products, chocolate products, ice creams, jams and jellies, pie fillings, salad dressings, soups and sweets.

lovage A European umbelliferous plant whose aromatic leaves and dried seeds are used as herbs to impart a celery-like flavour to salads and savoury dishes.

low-calorie drink Any drink that contains no more than 40 kcal or 147 kJ/100 ml per serving. Such drinks can help slimming or weight control only as part of a calorie-controlled diet.

low-calorie food Any food that contains no more than 40 kcal or 147 kJ/100 g per serving. Such foods can help slimming or weight control only as part of a calorie-controlled diet.

low-fat spread See **margarine**.

lutein (E161b) A **xanthophyll** pigment that occurs naturally in marigolds and egg yolks. It is used to impart a yellow or orange colour to foods, and may be fed to chickens to darken the colour of the yolks of their eggs.

lycopene (E160d) A **carotenoid** pigment that occurs naturally in tomatoes, from which it is extracted. It has been used as a red colouring agent in foods.

mace A spice made from the papery outer husks of **nutmeg**, whose flavour it resembles. It is used either as blades or ground into a powder in mulled wines, hot dishes and béchamel sauce.

MAFF Abbreviation of **Ministry of Agriculture, Fisheries and Food**.

magnesia Alternative name for **magnesium oxide**.

magnesite Alternative name for **magnesium carbonate**.

magnesium A light, metallic element that is an essential part of the green plant pigment **chlorophyll** and an important trace element in the human diet. Several magnesium compounds are used as food additives (see the following articles).

magnesium carbonate (504; also called **magnesite**) A mineral employed as an **acidity regulator**, anti-bleaching agent, **anti-caking agent** and **base**. It is used in some canned peas, ice creams, icing sugar, table salt, sour cream and wafer biscuits.

magnesium hydrogen metasilicate Alternative name for **talc**.

magnesium hydroxide (528) An alkaline mineral used as a **processing aid** in sugar refining and in making some types of **caramel**. It can be found in some canned vegetables and cocoa products.

magnesium oxide (530; also called **magnesia)** A mineral **base**, employed as an **anti-caking** agent in some canned peas, cocoa products and dairy products.

magnesium silicate, synthetic (553a) A synthetic **anti-caking agent** employed also as a **glazing agent** and **release agent** (for sweets) and for dusting such foods as chewing gum and rice. It can be found in crisps, icing sugar, packet noodles, table salt and vanilla powder.

magnesium stearate (572) A synthetic substance employed as an **anti-caking agent**, **emulsifier** and **release agent**. It can be found in dehydrated foods and hard sweets. It is not recommended for foods containing starch, and is banned in the US.

magnesium sulphate (518; also called **Epsom salts)** A soluble mineral salt employed as a **firming agent** and to provide **magnesium** as a dietary supplement. It is also used to adjust the composition of water in brewing. In large quantities magnesium sulphate acts as a laxative. It is not recommended for people with kidney disorders.

magnesium trisilicate (553a) A mineral substance with the same properties and uses as **magnesium silicate, synthetic**.

DL-malic acid; L-malic acid (296) An **organic acid** that occurs naturally in green apples and other fruits, employed as an **acidity regulator** and **flavouring**. It can be found in canned fruits and vegetables, frozen vegetables, jams and jellies, potato snacks, soft drinks and wine. The DL- form is not recommended in foods intended for babies and young children because it is not known whether they can metabolize both forms of malic acid.

maltodextrin (also called **glucose**, **glucose syrup** or **glucose polymer**) A substance made up of small chains of **glucose** units, which is produced during the commercial breakdown of **starch**. Maltodextrins are used as **thickeners** and **bulking agents**. They are less sweet than glucose or **sucrose** and can be used in greater amounts without making the product oversweet.

maltol (636) A substance that occurs naturally in malt and tree bark, but made synthetically for the food industry. It is used as a **flavouring** agent to impart a 'fresh-baked' taste to bread and cakes, and to enhance other flavourings. It has the property of making sweet foods taste sweeter, and so is added to foods instead of some of the sugar normally used. It can be found in baked goods, chewing gum, ice creams, jams and soft drinks. It is banned for use in foods intended for babies and young children.

maltose (also called **malt sugar**) A sugar that occurs in malt (germinated barley) and other germinating cereals, used as a source of **glucose**, which it forms on **hydrolysis**.

malt sugar Alternative name for **maltose**.

malt vinegar See **vinegar**.

manna sugar Alternative name for **mannitol**.

mannite Alternative name for **mannitol**.

mannitol (**E421**; also called **manna sugar**; **mannite**) A **sweetener** and **humectant** that occurs in pine wood and seaweed known as manna, from which it is extracted. It is also made synthetically by **hydrogenation** of **invert sugar**. It is not as sweet as **sucrose** and for this reason is used in foods that may be described as 'sugar-free'. It is also employed as an **anti-caking agent** and **release agent**. It can be found in chewing gum, desserts, ice creams and sweets. Mannitol can have a laxative effect and cause **hypersensitivity** reactions in susceptible people. It is not recommended in foods intended for babies and young children.

manufacturer According to the **Food Labelling Regulations**, the name and address of the manufacturer must appear on the labels of all pre-packed foods.

margarine A semi-solid fat produced from fish or vegetable oils that have been hydrogenated. A typical ordinary margarine consists of **hydrogenated** oils (fat), buttermilk (up to 10%), skimmed milk, **colouring**, vitamins A and D (a statutory requirement, to make margarine nutritionally similar to butter), **emulsifiers** (e.g. **lecithin**) and water (up to 16%), which are heated and churned together. Salt may also be added. Low-fat spreads, which cannot be described as margarine, contain only half the fat and energy of ordinary margarine and proportionally more water, which makes them unsuitable for cooking.

marigold A flower renowned for its yellow colour, which is due to the presence of **xanthophyll** pigments such as cryptoxanthin, used as food colourants. The petals and leaves may also be used in salads.

marjoram (also called **oregano**; **sweet marjoram**) A Mediterranean labiate plant with sweet-smelling leaves and a flavour reminiscent of nutmeg. It is used in salads or dried for use as a herb in savoury dishes, particularly in pizzas and stuffings for roast pork.

marmalade A type of **jam** made using the flesh and skins of citrus fruit, particularly oranges. By law marmalade must contain 60% added sugar, at least 20% citrus fruit and 7.5% citrus peel. The fruit may have been treated with **sulphur dioxide**, although this does not have to be declared on the label. **Colouring** may also be added. The type of cut of peel must be declared on the label, e.g. thick or thin peel. Reduced sugar marmalades contain 30–35% added sugar and may also contain **preservatives** and **sweeteners**.

maximum level The highest level permitted for specific additives in specific foods. These levels are set by the Ministry of Agriculture, Fisheries and Food on the advice of the **Food Advisory Committee**. The maximum levels are laid down in the regulations dealing with additives in food, such as the **Antioxidants in Food Regulations**.

mayonnaise A thick, creamy sauce made from an **emulsion** of oil and vinegar combined with egg yolk (which acts as an **emulsifier**) and flavourings, e.g. lemon juice. Mayonnaise is traditionally served with salad, lobster and vegetables, such as asparagus and globe artichokes. Commercially produced mayonnaise contains **preservatives**, emulsifiers and **stabilizers**.

MDGs Abbreviation of **mono- and diglycerides of fatty acids**.

meat The edible flesh of various animals and birds such as beef, game, lamb, mutton, pork and veal. **Colourings**, **antioxidants** and **preservatives** are not permitted in fresh or frozen meat, with the exception of **sulphur dioxide** in mince during the summer in Scotland. The use of **tenderizers**, either by addition to the meat or by injecting the animal before slaughtering, must be declared on a notice near the meat or, in the case of pre-packed meat, on the label. The use of **vitamin C** and **nicotinic acid** to preserve the colour of fresh meat is not permitted because their use can mislead the customer over the freshness of the product. Additives used in animal feeds may also be carried over into the meat as may **antibiotics** and hormone residues. Organic meat, which is free from additives, antibiotics and hormones, is available in some areas. See also **poultry**.

meat extract A concentrated **flavouring** made by mincing and boiling meat and then skimming off the fat and filtering and reducing it down to a concentrated liquid. Meat extracts may contain added flavouring and **colourings** and they may also have a high salt content.

meat product Any of a variety of foods that contain meat and other added ingredients. Many meat products are legally required to contain a minimum level of lean meat, including beefburgers (52% lean meat), pork sausages (32%) and beef sausages (25%). The minimum meat content of products not set by legislation must still be declared on the label.

A variety of additives are permitted, including **flavour enhancers**, **flavourings**, **colourings** and **preservatives**. With the exception of vitamins C and E **antioxidants** are not permitted, although they may be carried over in other ingredients. **Polyphosphates** are often added to meat products to enable the manufacturer to add extra water.

In any product containing cooked or raw meat and added water there must be a label stating 'with not more than x% added water', where x is the maximum amount of added water. With products that contain uncooked, cured meat (e.g. bacon) and more than 10% of the weight is added water, there must also be a label stating 'with not more than x% added water', but in this case x is five times the amount added in excess of 10%.

Meat (Treatment) Regulations A set of regulations issued by the Ministry of Agriculture, Fisheries and Food that prohibit the use on any raw and unprocessed meat, intended for human consumption, of any added substance specified in the regulations.

Meaux mustard A French mustard made from a mixture of ground and half-ground seeds with a grainy texture and musty taste. Meaux mustard is sold in stoneware jars, corked and secured with sealing wax.

medicines By law, the labels on proprietary medicines must state the names and concentrations of pharmacologically active ingredients, together with a recommended dose (and any warning about the maximum permitted dose). Medicines obtained from a pharmacist on prescription have to be labelled with the name of the medicine and the dose. Neither has to carry the names of non-active ingredients. These may include **sweeteners** and **colouring** agents, common in children's medicines, which may cause a reaction in susceptible people.

mejing Alternative name for **monosodium glutamate**.

metabolism The biochemical processes that take place in the body, including the breakdown of food, the production and use of energy and the building up of body chemicals and tissues.

metatartaric acid (353) An organic **acid** employed as a **sequestrant**, principally to remove excess calcium salts from wine (in which it may be found). It is also used as an **antioxidant** and **synergist** for other antioxidants.

methanoic acid Alternative name for **formic acid**.

methocel Alternative name for **methylcellulose**

methylcellulose (E461; also called **cologel; methocel)** A **bulking agent** made from cellulose, also used as an **emulsifier**, **stabilizer** and **thickener**. It can be found in baked goods, foods for diabetics, jams and jellies, sauces and slimming foods. In excess it can cause flatulence and intestinal problems.

methyl 4-hydroxybenzoate (E218; also called **methyl paraben; methyl para-hydroxybenzoate)** A synthetic **preservative** used in a wide range of foods from beer and coffee essence to pickles and sauces. It is also used as a preservative for other food additives such as **artificial**

flavourings and **sweeteners**. It is not recommended for people who suffer from **aspirin sensitivity**, **asthma** or **hyperactivity**.

methyl 4-hydroxybenzoate, sodium salt (E219; also called **sodium methyl hydroxybenzoate**; **sodium methyl para-hydroxybenzoate**) A synthetic **preservative** made from **benzoic acid**, whose properties and uses are very similar to those of **methyl 4-hydroxybenzoate**.

methyl paraben Alternative name for **methyl 4-hydroxybenzoate**.

methyl para-hydroxybenzoate Alternative name for **methyl 4-hydroxybenzoate**.

microcrystalline cellulose (E460a) A chemically fragmented form of cellulose employed as a general all-round food additive. Its many uses are as an **anti-caking agent**, binder, **bulking agent**, dispersing agent, **stabilizer** and as a source of dietary fibre. Dried granular foods may be made by using microcrystalline cellulose, which absorbs the liquid present in the foods. It is used in high-fibre bread, low-calorie foods, imitation fruit pieces and spices, salad dressings, synthetic cream and whipped toppings. It is not permitted for use in foods intended for babies and young children.

microcrystalline wax, refined (907) A mineral wax extracted from petroleum, employed as a **glazing agent**, **release agent** and coating for pills. It is also an ingredient in chewing gum. It is banned in the US.

migraine A periodic headache that usually affects one side of the head and is often accompanied by nausea and sometimes vomiting. A migraine is sometimes preceded by visual disturbances such as sensitivity to light and double vision. Although stress is the common cause, dietary factors also play a part in precipitating attacks. The common dietary culprits are cheese, chocolate, alcohol and citrus fruit and the additives **tartrazine** and **benzoic acid**.

milk The liquid secreted from the mammary glands of mammals. All milk sold in the UK has been **pasteurized** to preserve it, with the exception of raw untreated milk, which is usually sold directly from accredited farms in bottles with a green top.

There are four different types of milk available, which are classified by their fat content and with coloured foil caps to identify them. The types are: Channel Island (gold top) has 4.8% fat; whole milk (silver top) – which may be homogenized to disperse the fat evenly rather than having a distinctive cream layer –

has 3.8% fat; semi-skimmed (silver and red striped top) has 1.5–1.8% fat; skimmed (silver and blue checked top) has only 0.1% fat. These milks are not permitted to contain additives.

The natural growth hormone bovine somatotrophin (BST) is secreted by all cows to regulate milk production and is found in very small amounts in milk. By injecting BST into cows it is possible to increase their milk yield. In the UK, trials are at present under way to evaluate this procedure. Although the Ministry of Agriculture, Fisheries and Food have assured the public that the presence of greater levels of BST in milk is safe. However, it is not possible to identify milk that has come from BST-treated cows.

Many varieties of dried milks do not contain additives, but care should be taken to read the ingredients list because some brands do contain **emulsifiers** and **anti-caking agents**.

mineral Any substance that is not of animal or vegetable origin, e.g. **calcium**, **iodine** and **iron**, that are essential nutrients in the diet, required for good health and growth. Several of the compounds of some minerals are employed as food additives, such as compounds of calcium, **magnesium**, **potassium** and **sodium**.

If a claim is to be made that a food is a rich and excellent source of a particular mineral, the amount of that food which could be reasonably expected to be eaten in one day must contain half of the recommended daily amount (RDA) of that particular mineral. The claim that a food contains minerals can only be made if a normal serving of the food contains at least one-sixth of the RDA for those minerals mentioned on the label. The label must also give the percentage of the RDA that the food provides and the number of servings per pack.

mineral hydrocarbons (905; also called **liquid paraffin)** Oily substances extracted from petroleum employed as **anti-foaming agents** in sugar production, **glazing agents** for adding a shine to fresh fruit and cheese rind, and binders for capsules and pills. They are sprayed on eggs to seal and preserve them, and used as ingredients of chewing gum and sweets. These hydrocarbons are also used to lubricate vessels and machinery employed in food processing.

In large quantities mineral hydrocarbons have a laxative effect and may prevent the intestinal absorption of fats and fat-soluble vitamins. Their use is under review in the UK, with the probable result that they will be banned from some, if not all, of the foods currently permitted to contain them.

Mineral Hydrocarbons in Food Regulations A set of regulations issued by the Ministry of Agriculture, Fisheries and Foods that prohibit, with certain exceptions, the use of any **mineral hydrocarbon** in the composition or preparation of food. They also lay down specifications for mineral hydrocarbons and the method of testing solid mineral hydrocarbons for the presence of polycyclic hydrocarbons.

The use of mineral hydrocarbons in dried fruit, citrus fruit, sugar confectionery, lubricants, the rind of cheese, eggs and chewing compounds is at present under review. It is probable that their use in some, if not all, of these foods may be banned in the future.

minimum durability See **datemark**.

Ministry of Agriculture, Fisheries and Food (**MAFF**) The department of the British government that is responsible for formulating and administering the laws that concern the production, processing, manufacturing, labelling and marketing of food. It does this with the aid of various committees, chief of which – in terms of the food industry – are the ministry's own **Food Advisory Committee** (FAC) and the **Committee on Toxicity of Chemicals in Food** (COT), which belongs to the Ministry of Health.

mint Any of several species of aromatic labiate plants of the northern hemisphere whose fresh or dried leaves are used as a herb and seasoning. Peppermint and spearmint are the most highly flavoured members of the group, used mainly to make mint sauce or jelly, to flavour boiled potatoes or peas and sweets and desserts. Mint is also made into a tisane or herbal tea.

miscellaneous additives in food   A group of about 150 additives that are permitted in foods for a variety of purposes, and which do not fit into the other main categories of additives. Many of them are used as **processing aids**. See also **Miscellaneous Additives in Food Regulations**.

Miscellaneous Additives in Food Regulations   A set of regulations issued by the Ministry of Agriculture, Fisheries and Food that control 15 classes of food additives, and for certain miscellaneous additives specify the foods in which they may be used. The classes are: **acids**, **anti-caking** and **anti-foaming agents**, **bases**, **buffers**, **firming** and **glazing agents**, **humectants**, **liquid freezants**, **packaging gases**, **propellants**, **release agents**, **sequestrants**, **bulking aids** and **flavour modifiers**.

modified starch   Chemically **starch** is a **polysaccharide** made up of thousands of **glucose** units, which can be released as the simple sugar

164

or its compounds by modifying the starch. For instance, treating starch with an acid or an alkali brings about **hydrolysis** with the formation of sugars.

Modified starches are used extensively in the food industry to thicken foods and prevent watery separation. They also function as **emulsifiers** and **anti-caking agents**. Although modified starches are not subject to any legal control, their use is under review and may be more controlled in the future with certain types being allocated **E numbers**.

mono- and diacetyltartaric acid esters of mono- and diglycerides of fatty acids (E472e) Synthetic **emulsifiers** and **stabilizers** used in some chocolate drinks, cheesecake mixes, crisps, gravy granules and fats used in bread-making.

mono- and diglycerides of fatty acids (MDGs) (E471; also called **glyceryl monopalmitate** or **dipalmitate; glyceryl mono-oleate** or **dioleate; glyceryl monostearate** or **distearate**) Synthetic **emulsifiers** and **stabilizers** made from **glycerol** (glycerin). They are extensively used in the food industry in a wide range of products, including aerosol creams, baked goods, chocolate drinks, crisps, custard powders, margarine and powdered potato products.

monocalcium benzoate Alternative name for **calcium benzoate**.

monocalcium citrate Alternative name for **calcium citrate**.

monocalcium orthophosphate Alternative name for **calcium tetrahydrogen diorthophosphate**.

monoethanolamine Alternative name for **2-aminoethanol**.

monopotassium citrate Alternative name for **potassium dihydrogen citrate**.

monopotassium glutamate Alternative name for **potassium hydrogen L-glutamate**.

monopotassium phosphate Alternative name for **potassium dihydrogen orthophosphate**.

monopotassium L-(+)-tartrate (**E336**; also called **cream of tartar**; **potassium acid tartrate**; **potassium hydrogen tartrate**) An acidic salt, employed as a **buffer**, **emulsifying salt** and **raising agent** for flour and as a **synergist** for **antioxidants**. It is a by-product of winemaking and is also used in some cheese products, jellies, lemon dessert mixes, soft drinks and sweets. It is not recommended for people with kidney disorders.

monosaccharide A simple sugar such as **fructose** or **glucose**, as opposed to more complex **carbohydrates** such as **disaccharides** and **polysaccharides**.

monosodium citrate Alternative name for **sodium dihydrogen citrate**.

monosodium glutamate (MSG) (621; also called **aji-no-moto**; **mejing**; **sodium hydrogen L-glutamate**; **ve-tsin)** The sodium salt of the amino acid **glutamic acid**. It is a **flavour enhancer**, one of the best-known food additives, extracted from fermented soya beans or made synthetically by fermenting molasses or starch. It also serves as a salt substitute. It is used in a wide range of mostly savoury foods, such as pork products (cured ham, luncheon meat, pies, sausages), processed cheese and packet soups. It has been associated with intolerance symptoms in some susceptible people, such as **Chinese restaurant syndrome**. It is not permitted in foods intended for babies.

monosodium L-(+)-tartrate; disodium L-(+)-tartrate (E335; also called **sodium L-(+)-tartrate)** Acid salts, employed as **acidity regulators**, **antioxidants**, **buffers**, **emulsifying salts**, **sequestrants** and **synergists** for other antioxidants. They are used in some cheese products, fizzy drinks, jams and jellies, and sweets.

MSG Abbreviation for **monosodium glutamate**.

mustard A hot condiment made from the dried and ground seeds of various Eurasian brassica plants. Commercial ready-made English mustard consists of a paste made from mustard powder (known commercially as mustard flower) and water, with added salt, sugar, colouring, flavouring and stabilizer. There are also various other types of traditional mustard, often containing vinegar, e.g. **American**, **Bordeaux**, **Dijon** and **German mustards**.

mutagen A substance that causes a mutation, which is a permanent change in the genetic material of an organism's cells. In body cells, this can theoretically lead to **cancer**; in reproductive cells, it can lead to inherited abnormalities or birth defects.

name The name of a food must be clearly shown on its label. For some foods, such as sugar, wholemeal bread, yoghurt and fruit, the names which must be used are laid down by law and have a legal definition. In some cases, such as melons and potatoes, the species or variety must be shown. Certain foods have customary names which are not defined by law, but are understood by most people, e.g. museli, jam tart or pizza.

New foods or foods which are not widely known must have a name or accompanying description, which explains clearly what they are, e.g. 'a hot chocolate drink'. A trade mark, brand, fancy or invented name cannot be used instead of a clear name or description, it must appear with a name. The name must in no way mislead the customer and when a product has been processed it must state this clearly, e.g. 'smoked haddock', 'UHT milk' or 'dried vegetables'.

nasturtium A cruciferous plant with yellow or orange flowers, related to watercress. Its seeds are sometimes used as a flavouring or in pickles.

natural A term that is used in its strictest sense to describe unprocessed, wholesome food. A less restrictive definition has been suggested by the **Food Advisory Committee**, which is 'to describe single foods, of a traditional nature to which nothing has been added and which have been subjected only to such processing as to render them suitable for human consumption'. Processes such as **freezing**, concentration, fermentation, **pasteurization**, **sterilization**, smoking (without chemicals) and traditional cooking processes, e.g. baking, roasting and blanching, would all fit this definition. Bleaching, oxidation, smoking (with chemicals), tenderizing (with chemicals), **hydrogenation** and similar processes would not. For single ingredient foods, e.g. cheese, yoghurt and butter, acceptable processing would be that which is strictly necessary to produce the final product.

natural colour A **colouring** that has been obtained from recognized food sources by appropriate physical processing, including distillation and **solvent** extraction or by traditional food preparation. See also **artificial colour**.

natural flavour A **flavouring** that has been obtained from recognized food sources by appropriate physical processing, including distillation and **solvent** extraction or by traditional food preparation. A flavour should only be described as natural if it is derived wholly from the named food source. See also **artificial flavour**.

natural green 3 Alternative name for **chlorophyll**.

nature identical A description applied to a substance that, although synthetic, is chemically identical to a natural product. For example, in the same amounts, **ascorbic acid** (vitamin C) has exactly the same healthful effects in the body after it is ingested whether it is derived from lemons or a biochemist's laboratory.

net quantity In the labelling of a pre-packed food, the actual amount (usually weight) of the product excluding any packaging. The 'e' next to the net quantity means that the EC-based 'average' system of quantity control applies and that the actual quantity may be slightly above or below the given figure. Only very limited variations are acceptable. Where the number of items in the pack is of more use the label must show the number of items rather than the weight or volume, although both can be used, e.g. eggs and saccharin tablets.

niacin Alternative name for **nicotinic acid**.

nicotinamide Alternative name for **nicotinic acid**.

nicotinic acid (375; also called niacin; nicotinamide) A B complex vitamin, necessary in the diet to release energy from food. Foods rich in nicotinic acid include liver, yeast extracts, meat, fish, peanuts, bread, cereals, milk, cheese and eggs. It is made synthetically for use in the food industry, in which it is used as a vitamin supplement and colour preservative. It is added to all white flour and also to some breakfast cereals. A diet deficient in nicotinic acid causes the disorder pellagra.

nisin (234) An **antibiotic** produced by a *Streptococcus* bacterium, produced naturally in some cheeses. It may be found in cheeses and clotted cream, and be added as a preservative to some canned foods. It is banned in the US.

nitrates and nitrites Salts of nitrous and nitric acids, commonly used as **preservatives** for fish, meat and meat products. A nitrate usually changes to nitrite in food, and it is the nitrite that is the more effective preservative. They include **potassium nitrite**, **potassium nitrate** (saltpetre), **sodium nitrite** and **sodium nitrate** (Chile saltpetre). In the body, nitrites may form chemicals called nitrosamines, which are known **carcinogens**. However, the danger of food poisoning, particularly botulism, from bad meat is so great that nitrites and nitrates remain essential preservatives. They are banned in foods intended for babies under six months, and it is recommended that they should be avoided by children with a history of **hyperactivity**.

nitrogen An unreactive gas that makes up about 80% of air, from which it is extracted. It is used as an inert packaging gas and **propellant**, and liquid nitrogen is a **freezant**.

nitrous oxide (also called **dinitrogen oxide**; **laughing gas**) A relatively unreactive gas employed as an anaesthetic and as an **propellant** in aerosols of dairy products, e.g. whipped creams and toppings.

non-brewed condiment See **vinegar**.

non-dairy ice cream An ice cream that does not contain milk fat, butter or butter oil. The label should state clearly that the ice cream 'contains vegetable fat' or 'contains non-milk fat'. A variety of vegetable fats are used, many of which are high in saturated fatty acids.

norbixin Alternative name for **annatto**.

nutmeg An evergreen tree native to the East Indies, but now grown throughout the tropics for its hard aromatic seeds. It is used as a flavouring, whole or ground into a powder, in a wide variety of both savoury and sweet dishes, including vegetables, cheese dishes, milk puddings, custards and cakes. The husks of the seeds are used to make **mace**.

nutrient A component of food that can be digested and absorbed by the body to provide energy and the raw materials for growth, repair and reproduction. The major nutrients are **carbohydrate**, **fat**, **protein**, **vitamins** and **minerals**. The purpose of a balanced diet is to provide all the necessary nutrients in the correct amounts. Lack of one or more nutrients in the diet can lead to malnutrition and possible deficiency diseases, but equally too much of some nutrients can cause ill health too. No one food provides all the nutrients in the correct amounts (except breast-milk for babies), and therefore a wide variety of foods must be eaten to ensure a healthy, balanced diet.

nutritional claim The claim made on a label about the nutritional benefits of the food, e.g. 'high in fibre' or 'low in fat'. The food labelling laws ensure that claims are not misleading and in certain instances they lay down more specific controls for some claims. See APPENDIX I, ADDITIVE-FREE SHOPPING.

nutritional labelling A declaration on a food label of the energy and nutrient content. Although not required by law to give the nutritional information about a food, many manufacturers now use some form of nutritional labelling. Under the heading of 'nutrition information' may be listed the energy, protein, fat and carbohydrate content, the quantities of sugars, starch and dietary fibre, a breakdown of total fat into saturated, polyunsaturated and monounsaturated fatty acids, sodium, vitamin and mineral contents may also be given. See APPENDIX I, ADDITIVE-FREE SHOPPING.

nuts Dry, usually single-seeded fruits of various shrubs and trees or fruits that resemble them by having a hard shell and an edible kernel (such as walnuts and peanuts or groundnuts). Most nuts are rich in protein and oily fats, which is why they often figure in vegetarian diets.

octadecanoic acid Alternative name for **stearic acid**.

octadecylamine acetate Alternative name for **octadecyl ammonium acetate**.

octyl gallate (E311) A synthetic organic compound employed as an **antioxidant** by itself or in combination with other gallates. It is used in cooking fats, oils, margarine and foods prepared using them (such as breakfast cereals). It may cause gastric problems in people who suffer from **aspirin sensitivity** or **asthma** and is not recommended for children with a history of **hyperactivity**. Octyl gallate cannot be used in foods intended for babies or young children, and is banned in the US.

oedema The medical term for a swelling, applied to a part of the body that is swollen because of an accumulation of fluid in the tissues. It is a symptom of **angioedema**, **urticaria** and some **food allergies**.

oil A liquid **fat** derived from animals, such as fish, or plant tissues (usually seeds). Chemically they are glycerides (**glycerol** esters) of fatty acids. Common sources of vegetable oils include sesame seeds, olives, sunflower seeds, rapeseed and walnuts. Most vegetable oils are unsaturated or polyunsaturated, with the exception of coconut oil and palm oil, which (like most animal fats) are saturated. Oils can be treated with **hydrogen** to make solid fats such as cooking fat and margarine.

onion A plant grown for its edible bulb, which has a characteristic pungent flavour. Onions may be eaten raw or cooked, preserved by pickling, or dried and flaked for use as a savoury flavouring.

orange A sweet-tasting citrus fruit, eaten as a fresh fruit, in jams (marmalade) and as orange juice. It owes its colour to **carotene** pigments, which are sometimes extracted from oranges for use as a food colouring agent.

oregano Alternative name for **marjoram**.

organic acid An **acid** that is an organic compound based on carbon (e.g. **acetic** [ethanoic] **acid**), as opposed to an inorganic or mineral acid (e.g. **hydrochloric acid**). Organic acids tend to be weaker and less poisonous than inorganic ones. As with all acids, the molecules of organic acids contain one or more hydrogen atoms that can be released to form **salts** or **esters**.

organic food Any fruit, vegetable or animal product that has been produced without the use of chemical fertilizers or pesticides, or in the case of animals without the use of hormones or antibiotics. Organic foods are bought not only to avoid such chemicals, but also because of a preferred taste and because they are considered to be nutritionally superior to non-organic foods. However, the few studies that have been conducted to verify this have been unable to establish any nutritional difference.

There are many symbols under which organic foods may be sold including the Soil Association symbol, the Organic Farmers and Growers and the Organic Grower's Association. The first national standards for organic food production have recently been drawn up, and with time consumers should be able to buy organic food confident that it meets certain specified criteria.

orthophenylphenol Alternative name for **2-hydroxybiphenyl**.

orthophosphoric acid (E338; also called **phosphoric acid)** An inorganic **acid** employed as an **acidity regulator**, **sequestrant** and **synergist**. It is also used to retain sugars in malting and to compensate for variations in the water supply in brewing. It may be found in beer, cheese products, fats, frozen dairy products, jams, meat products, soft drinks and sweets.

oxidatively polymerized soya bean oil (also called **brown soya oil**) A thick liquid made by passing oxygen through hot soya bean oil. It is made into an **emulsion** for greasing baking tins, and so can be found as traces on the surface of biscuits, pies and other baked goods.

oxygen A colourless, odourless gas that makes up about 20% of air, from which it is extracted. It may be used as a packaging gas and in the manufacture of **modified starch**.

oxystearin A mixture of glycerides (**glycerol** esters) of oxidized **stearic acids** that occurs in animal fats, from which it is extracted. It is employed as an **anti-foaming agent** and **sequestrant**. It can be found in some cooking oils, which it prevents from solidifying at low temperatures.

packaging gas A gas that is included with a food product to control the 'atmosphere' inside the package. For example, the unreactive gas **nitrogen** may be used in packaging a dehydrated food to exclude oxygen (air) or moisture, which would otherwise damage or promote the growth of microorganisms. **Carbon dioxide** may be used for a similar purpose. Other gases used in packages include hydrogen and oxygen.

6–O-palmitoyl-L-ascorbic acid (**E304**; also called **ascorbyl palmitate**) A synthetic compound employed as an **antioxidant** and **anti-browning agent** to prevent cut fruits from turning brown. Unlike **ascorbic acid** it dissolves in fats. It is used in pork pies, sausages and stock cubes.

pantothenic acid One of the B group of vitamins, needed in the body for proper enzyme action in cells. Foods rich in pantothenic acid include eggs, liver, whole-grain cereals and yeast. Deficiency of the vitamin may result in skin disorders.

papaya (also called **pawpaw**) An evergreen tree native to the West Indies, grown for its large edible fruits which contain a sweet yellow flesh. Papaya contains the enzyme papain, which, in powder or leaf form, can be used as a meat **tenderizer**.

paprika A mild spice and seasoning made by powdering the dried fruits of a sweet form of red pepper grown in central Europe. The spice is mild and used in a variety of dishes from goulash to a garnish on canapés. The same fruit yields the orange pigment **capsanthin** (or capsorubin), used as a food colouring agent.

parboil To cook something incompletely by boiling it for a short time, usually as a preliminary to preserving it or to completion of cooking by another method.

parsley An umbelliferous plant native to southern Europe, widely grown for its aromatic leaves which are used (fresh or dried) in salads, sauces and savoury dishes.

pasteurization A method of treating a liquid such as milk or fruit juice by heating it to below its boiling point for a specified time in order to kill any bacteria present. Milk is heated to 63–66°C for up to 30 minutes or to 72°C for 15 seconds to pasteurize it.

pastry mix A mixture of flour and fat and sometimes egg that is bound together with water. There are several kinds of pastry including shortcrust, flaky, suetcrust, hot water crust, choux and fillo, which differ from each other mainly in the method of incorporating the fat. Frozen ready-to-use pastries are available, some using wholemeal flour (sometimes organically grown), and others white flour. Few additives are used, although some varieties contain **emulsifiers**, **antioxidants** and **colourings**.

paté Finely minced fish, meat (often liver) or vegetables, blended with fat and sometimes herbs, spices or garlic, used as a spread or sandwich filling.

patent blue V (E131; also called **acid blue 3)** A **coal tar dye** used to impart a blue-violet colour to foods. It is used in some canned vegetables, deserts, ice creams, Scotch eggs, soft drinks and sweets. It should be avoided by anybody with a history of allergy and is not recommended for children with a history of **hyperactivity**.

peanut butter A brownish confection and sandwich filling made from finely ground peanuts (groundnuts), salt, sugar, or a **sweetener**, and sometimes blended with vegetable oil. It may contain **emulsifiers**, but it is possible to buy varieties without any salt, sugar or additives. Peanuts stored in poor conditions may be affected by strains of an *Aspergillus* fungus, which produce poisonous **aflatoxins**. However, these very rarely turn up in peanut products intended for human consumption.

pectin (E440a) An **emulsifier**, **gelling agent**, **thickening agent** and **stabilizer**, which occurs in ripe fruit and is extracted commercially from the pulp remaining after making cider or orange juice. It may be found in a wide range of foods, including beverages, desserts, flavoured yoghurts, ice creams, jams and jellies, sweets and syrups. Ingesting large quantities may cause flatulence.

pentapotassium triphosphate (E450b; also called **potassium tripolyphosphate)** A synthetic polyphosphate employed as a **buffer**, **emulsifier**, **sequestrant** and **stabilizer**. It is also used to bind water to the proteins in meat and meat products to make them more tender. It can also be found in bread, cheese spreads and processed cheeses.

pentasodium triphosphate (E450b; also called **sodium tripolyphosphate**; **STPP**) A synthetic polyphosphate employed as a **buffer**, **emulsifier**, **sequestrant** and **stabilizer**. It is also used to bind water to the proteins in meat and meat products to make them more tender. It may be found in some condensed milk, custard powder, processed cheeses and packet soups as well as in a variety of meat products.

pepper A white pepper, used as a hot condiment and seasoning, made from the full-ripened, dried seeds (without their husks) of the pepper plant, either whole or ground into a fine powder. See also **black peppercorn**; **green peppercorn**.

peppercorn The dried berry of the **pepper** plant. See **black peppercorn**; **green peppercorn**.

peppermint A pungent flavouring made from an oil extracted from the leaves of a plant of the mint family. See also **mint**.

pesticide A chemical used to kill pests, including fungicides (moulds and fungi), insecticides (insects) and weed killers. Most pesticide are highly poisonous and traces of them may be left on foods after harvesting or after treatment in store.

phenyl benzene Alternative name for **biphenyl**.

phosphatides Alternative name for **phospholipids**.

phosphoric acid Alternative name for **orthophosphoric acid**.

phospholipids (also called **phosphatides**) Naturally occurring fat-like substances that are major components of cell membranes. They consist of a compound such as **glycerol** that has formed an **ester** with both a fatty acid and phosphoric acid. This chemical structure enables them to bind a fatty substance to water, and so form an **emulsion**. **Lecithin**, a common emulsifier, is a phospholipid.

phosphorus A non-metallic element that is an essential nutrient necessary for healthy blood, bones and teeth, in which it occurs as calcium phosphate. A normal balanced diet contains sufficient phosphorus for the body's needs because it is present in a wide variety of foods.

pickle A fresh or lightly cooked vegetable or vegetables, fruit or fruits preserved in brine (salt solution), vinegar (**acetic acid**) or **lactic acid**, often with added herbs or spices. Cauliflower, cucumber and onions have long been preserved in this way. Some pickles, such as mustard pickle (piccalilli) and sweet pickle, also incorporate a spicy sauce. Artificial preservatives are also common in commercially made pickles.

pigment rubine (E180; also called **lithol rubine BK)**   An **azo dye** employed as a red **colouring** agent in the rinds of Edam-like cheeses, its only permitted use in the UK and the EC. It is banned in the US.

place of origin   The location where the product has been made. It is sometimes included on the label if the name of the food would otherwise be misleading. One would not expect all Swiss rolls to be made in Switzerland or all Bakewell tarts in Bakewell, but Devon fudge made in Germany would be considered misleading if the place of origin was not stated on the label.

plaster of Paris   Alternative name for **calcium sulphate**.

polydextrose   A substance similar to cellulose, employed as a **bulking agent** and **thickener**. It is used in some 'diet' foods such as desserts and soft drinks, and can also be found in baked goods, instant puddings and sweets. It is not permitted in foods intended for babies and young children.

polyglycerol esters of fatty acids (E474) A synthetic **emulsifier** and **stabilizer** made from animal fats or vegetable oils. It is used in some baked products, chocolate, packet cakes and pudding mixes and crisps.

polyglycerol esters of polycondensed fatty acids of castor oil (476; also called polyglycerol polyricinoleate) A synthetic **emulsifier** and **stabilizer** made from castor oil, used also to grease baking tins. It is commonly used in chocolate coatings for biscuits, cakes and sweets. It is banned in the US.

polyglycerol polyricinoleate Alternative name for **polyglycerol esters of polycondensed fatty acids of castor oil**.

polyoxyethylene (20) sorbitan monolaurate (432; also called polysorbate 20, tween 20) A synthetic mixture of substances made from lauric acid and **sorbitol**, employed as a dispersing agent, **emulsifier** and **stabilizer**. It is found in some bread and cake mixes and toppings, baked goods, banned in some European countries, although not in the UK.

polyoxyethylene (20) sorbitan mono-oleate (433; also called polysorbate 80; tween 80) A synthetic mixture of substances made from oleic acid and **sorbitol**, employed as an **anti-foaming agent** (in sugar extraction from beet), **emulsifier** and **stabilizer**. It is used to retain the moisture in bread and doughnuts, and to prevent artificial whipped cream from separating. It is found in cakes, custard, icing, non-dairy milk substitute and sweets. It is banned in some European countries, although not in the UK.

polyoxyethylene (20) sorbitan monopalmitate (434; also called polysorbate 40; tween 40) A synthetic mixture of substances made from palmitic acid and **sorbitol**, employed as an **anti-foaming agent**, dispersing agent, **emulsifier** and **stabilizer**. It is used in some bread, cakes, cake mixes, custard, desserts, doughnuts, ice cream, icing, non-dairy milk substitute, sweets and whipped toppings. It is banned in some European countries, although not in the UK.

polyoxyethylene (20) sorbitan monostearate (435; also called polysorbate 60; tween 60) A synthetic mixture of substances made from **stearic acid** and **sorbitol**, employed principally as an **emulsifier** and **stabilizer**. It is used to prevent the oil from separating from artificial cream, mayonnaise and flavourings in sweets. It can be found in bread, cakes, cake mixes, doughnuts, icing, non-dairy milk substitute and sweets. It is banned in some European countries, although not in the UK.

polyoxyethylene (20) sorbitan tristearate (436; also called **polysorbate 65; tween 65)** A synthetic substance made from **stearic acid** and **sorbitol**, employed as an **anti-foaming agent**, **emulsifier** and **stabilizer**. It is used to prevent the oil separating from frozen desserts, artificial whipped cream and flavourings in sweets. It can be found in bread, cakes and doughnuts (in which it retains moisture), dehydrated foods, frozen desserts, ice cream, non-dairy milk substitutes and whipped toppings. It is banned in some European countries, although not in the UK.

polyoxyethylene (8) stearate (430; also called **polyoxyl (8) stearate)** A synthetic **emulsifier** and **stabilizer** used to retain the apparent freshness of baked goods and dessert toppings. It has been associated with skin allergies in susceptible people. It is banned in the US and most EC countries, although not in the UK.

polyoxyethylene (40) stearate (431; also called **polyoxyl 40 stearate)** A synthetic **emulsifier** which is added to bread and other baked goods to make them retain their apparent freshness. It is banned in the US and most EC countries, although not in the UK.

polyphosphates, ammonium See **ammonium polyphosphates**.

polyphosphates, calcium See **calcium polyphosphates**.

polyphosphates, sodium See **sodium polyphosphates**.

polypropylene glycol esters of fatty acids See **propane-1,2-diol esters of fatty acids**.

polysaccharide A **carbohydrate** whose molecules consist of many simple **monosaccharide** sugar units linked together, usually in long chains. Polysaccharides include the plant products cellulose and **starch**, and glycogen (the form in which **glucose** is stored in the liver and tissues).

polysorbate 20 See **polyoxyethylene (20) sorbitan monolaurate**.

polysorbate 40 See **polyoxyethylene (20) sorbitan monopalmitate**.

polysorbate 60 See **polyoxyethylene (20) sorbitan monostearate**.

polysorbate 65 See **polyoxyethylene (20) sorbitan tristearate**.

polysorbate 80 See **polyoxyethylene (20) sorbitan mono-oleate**.

ponceau 4R (E124; also known as **cochineal red R)** An **azo dye** and **coal tar dye**, used as a red **colouring** agent. It is widely used and can be found in cake mixes, canned fruits, dessert toppings, ices, jams and jellies, salami, soups and sweets. It should be avoided by people with **aspirin sensitivity** or **asthma** and by children with a history of **hyperactivity**. It is banned in Norway.

poppy seed A small blue-grey seed of a type of poppy, with a nutty flavour. It is widely used in Jewish and central European cooking and as a flavoured coating on bread and rolls

potash alum Alternative name for **aluminium potassium sulphate**.

potassium A light, very reactive metallic element, essential in the body (e.g. for the proper functioning of nerves). A normal balanced diet contains sufficient potassium for the body's needs. All potassium salts are soluble in water, and for this reason the element is a constituent of many food additives (see the following articles).

potassium acetate (E261; also called **potassium ethanoate)** The potassium salt of **acetic (ethanoic) acid,** employed as an **acidity regulator, buffer** and preservative for natural food colours. It may be found in some soups and frozen vegetables. It should be avoided by people with kidney disorders.

potassium acid tartrate Alternative name for **monopotassium L-(+)-tartrate.**

potassium alginate (E402; also called **potassium polymannuronate)** A substance made from **alginic acid,** itself extracted from seaweed, which may occasionally be employed as an **emulsifier, gelling agent** and **stabilizer** as an alternative to the much cheaper sodium alginate. It is therefore useful for people on low-sodium diets, and may be found in some baked goods, beverages, desserts, salad dressings and sweets.

potassium aluminium sulphate Alternative name for **aluminium potassium sulphate.**

potassium benzoate (E212) The potassium salt of benzoic acid, employed as a **preservative** in some fruit juices, margarine, pickles and sauces, and to preserve other food additives. It should be avoided by people with allergic conditions such as aspirin **sensitivity, asthma** or

urticaria. Potassium benzoate is not recommended for children with a history of **hyperactivity**. It is banned in the US.

potassium bicarbonate Alternative name for **potassium hydrogen carbonate**.

potassium bromate (924) An inorganic salt employed until recently as an **improving agent** for flour in bread-making, where it helped to keep the dough aerated, and it was also used in making malt for brewing. It was removed from the list of permitted flour improvers in April 1990.

potassium carbonate (501) An **alkali** and **buffer**, together with **potassium hydrogen carbonate** (potassium bicarbonate), which is also included under the designation 501. These salts may be found in some cocoa products, custard powder and sweets.

potassium chloride (508) An inorganic salt employed as a **gelling agent** and as a substitute for common salt (sodium chloride) in low-salt products. It may be added to malt used in brewing to compensate for variations in the composition of the local water supply. It may be found in canned red kidney beans.

potassium citrate Alternative name for **tripotassium citrate**.

potassium dihydrogen citrate (E332; also called **monopotassium citrate**) A potassium salt of **citric acid** employed as a **buffer**, **emulsifier** and yeast food. It is used in dairy products (such as condensed milk, dried milk, UHT cream and processed cheese), artificially sweetened jams and jellies, and sweets.

potassium dihydrogen orthophosphate (E340a; also called **monopotassium phosphate**; **MKP**) A potassium salt of **orthophosphoric acid** employed as a **buffer**, **emulsifier**, **sequestrant** and **synergist**. It is also used as a yeast food in brewing and wine-making. It can be found in some dessert toppings, instant custard, and jelly and sauce mixes.

potassium ferrocyanide (536; also called **potassium hexacyanoferrate(II)**) An inorganic substance employed as an **anti-caking agent** in table salt and as a means of precipitating copper and iron compounds in wine. It is banned in the US.

potassium gluconate (577) The potassium salt of gluconic acid, employed as a **sequestrant** and yeast food. It is added to sliced apples and some sweets.

potassium hexacyanoferrate(II) Alternative name for **potassium ferrocyanide**.

potassium hydrogen carbonate (501; also called potassium bicarbonate) An acid salt that shares the designation and uses of **potassium carbonate**.

potassium hydrogen L-glutamate (622; also called monopotassium glutamate; MPG) A synthetic **flavour enhancer** occasionally employed as an alternative to the cheaper monosodium glutamate (MSG), especially in low-sodium foods. It is also used as a salt substitute. It has produced symptoms of **food allergy** or **food intolerance** in susceptible people and is not permitted in foods intended for babies. See also **Chinese restaurant syndrome**.

potassium hydrogen tartrate Alternative name for **monopotassium L-(+)-tartrate**.

potassium hydroxide (525; also called caustic potash) An **alkali** found in black olives, some cheese and cocoa products, and jams.

potassium lactate (E326) The potassium salt of **lactic acid**, employed as an **acidity regulator**, **buffer** and **synergist**. It is used in cheeses, ice cream, jams and jellies, low-fat spreads, soups and sweets.

potassium malate (351) The potassium salt of **malic acid**, employed as a **buffer**. It can be found in some jams, jellies and marmalade.

potassium metabisulphite (E224; also called **potassium pyrosulphite)** A synthetic **anti-oxidant, anti-browning agent, bleaching agent** and **preservative**. It is used in beer, cider and wine, desserts, dried and frozen vegetables, fruit juices, frozen prawns and shrimps, and milk products. It is also employed to bleach cod and sugar. It should be strictly avoided by people who have **asthma** or a history of **food aversion**, and it is not recommended for children who have a history of **hyperactivity**.

potassium nitrate (E252; also called **salt-petre)** An important **preservative** for meat and meat products, including canned, cured and pressed meats and sausages, in which it combats botulism. It is also used for fixing the colours of foods. In the body it is converted to potassium nitrite (see **nitrates and nitrites**). It should not be used in foods intended for babies and young children.

potassium nitrite (E249) A curing agent and **preservative** for smoked fish, meat and meat products, in which it is effective against botulism. It should not be used in foods intended for babies and young children. See **nitrates and nitrites**.

potassium phosphate dibasic Alternative name for **dipotassium hydrogen orthophosphate**.

potassium phosphate tribasic Alternative name for **tripotassium orthophosphate**.

potassium polymannuronate Alternative name for **potassium alginate**.

potassium polyphosphates (E450c) Synthetic salts that are employed as **emulsifiers**, **sequestrants** and **stabilizers**. They are also used to improve the texture of fish, meat and meat products, which they achieve by making the meat protein bind to water. They can be also found in bread, custard, processed cheeses and reduced-sugar jams. Sodium polyphosphates, which have the same properties and uses, are also included in the designation E450c.

potassium propionate (E283; also called **potassium propanate)** The potassium salt of **propionic** (propanoic) **acid**, employed as a **preservative**, particularly against the moulds that can cause sticky yellow patches in bread dough. It is used in some bread and other baked products, Christmas puddings and processed cheeses. It is not permitted in the US.

potassium pyrosulphite Alternative name for **potassium metabisulphite**.

potassium salts of fatty acids (E470) Substances that are chemically soaps, employed in the food industry as **anti-caking agents**, **emulsifiers** and **stabilizers**. They are used in some cake mixes, crisps, icing sugar and soups.

potassium sodium L-(+)-tartrate (E337; also called **sodium and potassium tartrate;** **sodium potassium tartrate; Rochelle salt)** An organic salt produced as a by-product of wine-making, employed as a **buffer, emulsifier, stabilizer** and **synergist**. It may be used in cheese products, jams and jellies, margarines, meat products and sweets.

potassium sorbate (E202) The potassium salt of **sorbic acid**, used as a **preservative** and fungicide, particularly in wine-making. It can be found in a wide range of foods, including baked goods, cheese and milk products, chocolate products, pie fillings and puddings, margarines, pickles, savoury dressings and soft drinks.

potassium sulphate (515) A mineral salt employed as a substitute for table salt (sodium chloride), particularly in low-sodium foods. It is also used in brewing.

potassium tripolyphosphate Alternative name for **pentapotassium triphosphate**.

poultry The meat of domestic fowl such as chicken, duck, goose and turkey. Only a small percentage of chicken is sold free-range, the majority are intensively reared. **Polyphosphates** may be added to frozen chickens to increase the water content of the meat, but the amount of water present is controlled by the Poultry Meat (Water Content) Regulation and is limited to 7.4%. Chickens are usually chilled with cold water, but it is possible to buy 'chill frozen' or 'dry-chilled' ones, which have been air-chilled without the addition of water. The water content of such chickens will be less than traditionally chilled chickens unless polyphosphates have been added.

The yellow colour of maize or corn fed chickens is due to **xanthophylls** in the feed or to the addition of **lutein** to dried feedstuffs. Most brands of cooked and flavoured chickens contain added **colourings** and **flavourings**, which are often artificial.

powdered cellulose Alternative name for **alpha-cellulose**.

ppm Abbreviation for parts per million, used to express very low concentrations. It is the unit to show how much of an additive is present in a food.

preservative Any substance added to food to destroy or prevent the growth of organisms that could contaminate or spoil the food. Some preservatives work against bacteria, such as the one that causes botulism (see **nitrates and nitrites**); others, such as **sulphur dioxide**, sulphites and sorbates, combat fungi and moulds; and still others, such as **benzoic acid** and benzoates, are effective against both. Undoubtedly the use of preservatives has made many foods, particularly fish, meat and meat products, much safer to eat. The penalty is that susceptible people, particularly those who suffer from a **food intolerance** or an allergy such as **aspirin sensitivity**, **asthma** or **urticaria**, are affected by some preservatives and should avoid them. In a sense **antioxidants**, which are used typically to prevent fat from oxidizing and going rancid, also act as preservatives.

Preservatives in Food Regulations A set of regulations issued by the Ministry of Agriculture, Fisheries and Food that control the use of **preservatives** in food. The regulations list the substances that are permitted and where appropriate they specify the foods in which they may be used and the maximum levels that can be added.

preserve Any fruit or vegetable that has been boiled with sugar to preserve it and to enhance its keeping properties. See also **jam**.

processed cheese A **cheese** that has been heated or **pasteurized** to stop it maturing or changing in any way. Processed cheese contains at least 50% dry matter and 40% fat. It is sold in foil-wrapped portions, often shaped in triangles, cubes or very thin slices. Separation of the fat is prevented by the addition of **emulsifiers**. **Flavourings**, acid and salt may also be added. Cheese spreads are similar except that they have a higher water content.

processed food A food that has not been prepared and cooked by the consumer but by the manufacturer. Processed food is used primarily for convenience, to save time and includes a wide range of products from single ingredients, e.g. frozen peas, to complete meals. Additives are used extensively in many processed foods as **processing aids**, to increase the shelf life and to improve the palatability of the food.

processing aids Any of a number of substances incorporated with a food to facilitate processing or manufacture, they include: **anti-foaming agents**, **release** or non-stick **agents**, **solvents**, **anti-caking agents** and **improving agents**. See also the INTRODUCTION page viii.

propane-1,2-diol alginate (**E405**; also called **alginate ester**; **propylene glycol alginate**) A synthetic substance made from **alginic acid**, which is itself made from seaweed, employed as an **emulsifier**, **stabilizer** and **thickener**. It is also used to maintain the head on beers and lagers. It can be found in some baked goods, beverages, canned vegetables, cheese products, ice creams, ice lollies, salad dressings, sauces and sweets.

propane-1,2-diol esters of fatty acids (E477; also called **propylene glycol esters of fatty acids**) Synthetic substances employed as **emulsifiers** and **stabilizers** in beverages, cake mixes, ice creams, instant desserts and toppings, meat products and sweets.

propellant An inert gas or volatile liquid incorporated under pressure into an aerosol to force out the contents. **Carbon dioxide**, **hydrogen** and **nitrogen** are used as propellants.

propionic acid (E280; also called **propanoic acid**) An organic **acid** employed as a **preservative** against fungi and moulds. It occurs naturally in some cheeses and is added to bread dough to prevent the formation of sticky yellow patches (due to a fungus). It can also be found in other baked goods and Christmas puddings.

propylene glycol (also called **propane-1,2-diol**) An organic liquid used as a **humectant** and solvent for other food additives. It is also the starting material for other propylene glycol (propane-1,2-diol) compounds used as additives. It can be found in some baked goods, ice cream, sweets and wine.

propylene glycol alginate   Alternative name for **propane-1,2-diol alginate**.

propylene glycol esters of fatty acids   Alternative name for **propane-1,2-diol esters of fatty acids**.

propyl gallate (E310; also called **propyl ester of gallic acid**; **propyl 3,4,5-trihydroxybenzoate**)   A synthetic organic compound employed as an **antioxidant**, particularly for fats and oils, and as a **synergist** for other antioxidants. It does not tolerate high temperatures and so is unsuitable for baked goods. It may be added to dried potato and the inner wrappers of cereals. It can be found in breakfast cereals, jellies, margarines, potato products and vegetable oils. It should be avoided by people with **asthma** and **aspirin sensitivity** and by children with a history of **hyperactivity**. In the UK it is not permitted in foods intended for babies and young children. It is banned in the USSR and some eastern European countries.

propyl 4-hydroxybenzoate (E216; also called **n-propyl p-hydroxybenzoate**; **propyl para-**

hydroxybenzoate) A widely used synthetic **preservative**, used in foods from beer and coffee to pickles and soft drinks. It is also employed to preserve other food additives. It is not recommended for people with **aspirin sensitivity** or **asthma**, or for children with a history of **hyperactivity**.

propyl 4-hydroxybenzoate, sodium salt (E217; also called **sodium n-propyl p-hydroxybenzoate**; **sodium propyl para-hydroxybenzoate)** A synthetic **preservative** with properties and uses similar to those of **propyl 4-hydroxybenzoate**.

propyl para-hydroxybenzoate Alternative name for **propyl hydroxybenzoate**.

protein The essential component of all living matter, made up of long chains of individual units called **amino acids**. The cells of our bones, muscles, skin, nails, hair and every other tissue are made up of proteins. It is constantly being broken down and replaced. In food it is broken down into its component amino acids during digestion, then absorbed and rearranged into new body protein.

pruritis The medical term for **itching**.

pteroyl-L-glutamic acid Alternative name for **folic acid**.

pyridoxine Alternative name for **vitamin B₆**.

quicklime Alternative name for **calcium oxide**.

quillaia Alternative name for **extract of quillaia**.

quinoline yellow (E104) A synthetic **coal tar dye**, employed to give a yellow or yellow-green colour to foods. It is found in some ice lollies, Scotch eggs, smoked fish and soft drinks. It is not recommended for children with a history of **hyperactivity**, and is banned in Canada, Japan, Norway and the US.

raising agent A substance used in cooking that, on its own or in the presence of another substance, generates bubbles of **carbon dioxide** gas, which make cakes and other baked goods rise. The traditional raising agent is **baking powder**, and other types include carbonates, hydrogen carbonates (bicarbonates) and some phosphates.

ready meal A type of **convenience food** that contains all the elements of a complete course, usually requiring only heating and not complete cooking.

red 2 Alternative name for **amaranth**.

red 2G (128) A synthetic **azo dye** and **coal tar dye**, employed to impart a red colour to jams, meat and meat products, and soft drinks. It will not withstand high temperatures or high acidity. It is not recommended for children with a history of **hyperactivity**. Red 2G is banned in most European countries, Australia, Japan and North America, although not in the UK.

reduced-calorie drink A fruit drink or soft drink in which some of the sugar, in the form of **sucrose**, has been replaced by less calorific natural sugars or **artificial sweeteners**. A reduced-calorie drink must contain no more than 75% of the calorific value of the standard product. Such drinks can help slimming or weight control, but only as part of a calorie-controlled diet.

reduced-calorie food A food in which the calorific value has been reduced, usually by replacing some or all of the sugar it contains with **artificial sweeteners**, or replacing digestible carbohydrates (e.g. starch-based ingredients) with indigestible **bulking agents**, often based on cellulose. A reduced-calorie food must contain no more than 75% of the calorific value of the standard product. Such foods can help in slimming or weight control, but only as part of a calorie-controlled diet.

refined microcrystalline wax (907) A mineral substance extracted from petroleum, employed as a **glazing agent** and **release agent**, and as a base for chewing gum.

release agent (also called **abherent**) A substance applied as a coating to cooking vessels, food processing machinery and sometimes the food itself to prevent food from sticking to surfaces. Common release agents include silicates and stearates.

rennet A substance obtained from the stomach lining of ruminants (usually calves), employed to curdle milk to make junket, or the curds for cheese-making. Its active ingredient is the **enzyme** rennin. Vegetarian cheese is made using a rennet-like substance from certain plants, e.g. cardoon.

rhinitis The medical term for a running nose, usually caused by inflammation accompanying a common cold, influenza or possibly an allergic condition. See **food allergy**.

rhodoxanthin (E161f) A naturally occurring **carotenoid** plant pigment obtained from the seeds of the yew tree, permitted as a yellow **colouring** agent; it is rarely used.

riboflavin (E101; also called **lactoflavin; vitamin B₂**) A B complex vitamin, necessary in the body for growth, the release of energy from food and for healthy skin and eyes. Foods rich in riboflavin include liver (and other offal), meat, dairy products, eggs and cereals (including breakfast cereals). A deficiency of the vitamin leads to skin disorders, cracked lips and an oversensitivity to light. Riboflavin is used in the food industry as a vitamin supplement and as and orange-yellow **colouring** agent. It can be found in processed cheeses and sauces. It is permitted as a colouring agent in foods intended for babies and young children, but limited to the amounts used as a vitamin supplement.

riboflavin–5′-phosphate (101a; also called **riboflavin–5′-[sodium phosphate])** A more expensive and more soluble form of vitamin B_2 made from **riboflavin**, used also as an orange or yellow food **colouring** agent. It can be found in breakfast cereals, condensed or dried milk, and jams. It is permitted as a colouring agent in foods intended for babies and young children, but limited to the amounts used as a vitamin supplement.

rice vinegar A Japanese vinegar made from fermented saké or rice wine. It has a sweet delicate flavour and is used particularly in sushi (Japanese dishes of rice and raw fish).

Rochelle salt Alternative name for **potassium sodium L-(+)-tartrate**.

rocket A cruciferous plant native to the Mediterranean region whose leaves have a slightly bitter, peppery flavour and are used in salads and as a herb.

rock salt A form of common **salt** (sodium chloride) that occurs naturally in underground deposits, usually purified by recrystallization for culinary use. It is essentially the same as sea salt or any other form of table salt.

rocou Alternative name for **annatto**.

rope A descriptive term for sticky yellow strands in **bread**, caused by a mould that forms in flour or dough. For example, the spores of some microorganisms of the genus *Bacillus* resist the heat of the baking process and create characteristic yellow patches and strands. Bread manufacturers use mould-inhibiting **preservatives**, e.g. **propionic acid** and its salts, to prevent the mould from forming.

rosemary An evergreen labiate shrub native to Europe, whose grey-green aromatic leaves are used, fresh or dried, as a savoury flavouring.

rose water A fragrant rose-flavoured water distilled from rose petals or made from essential rose oil. It is used in baking and in sweet dishes and is also an ingredient of Turkish Delight.

rubixanthin (E161d) A **xanthophyll** plant pigment that occurs in rosehips, which can be used as a yellow **colouring** agent for foods.

saccharin An **artificial sweetener** which is about 300 times as sweet as ordinary **sucrose**. It is not very soluble in water and so its sodium or calcium salt is normally used. It is employed instead of sugar in low-calorie or reduced-calorie foods, and as a sugar substitute in foods for people with **diabetes**. Saccharin does not contribute to tooth decay, but some people find that it has a bitter aftertaste. It is not permitted in foods intended for babies and young children.

saffron Alternative name for **crocin**.

sage (also called **salvia**) A labiate plant from the Mediterranean region, grown for its aromatic leaves which have a strong slightly bitter flavour. It is used as a herb and savoury flavouring, traditionally as a stuffing made with onions and in Derby cheese.

salad cream A creamy sauce for salads traditionally made from egg yolks, vegetable oil and vinegar. Commercial version must by law have vegetable oil and egg, and they may also contain an **emulsifier** and **stabilizer** in addition to other additives. There are brands available which are made without salt, sugar and any additive. See also **mayonnaise**.

salicylate A salt of salicylic acid, most commonly encountered as its acetyl derivative aspirin. Salicylates occur naturally in such foods as almonds, apricots, apples, oranges, cucumber, peaches, plums, prunes, tangerines, tomatoes and soft drinks. **Hyperactive** children are often recommended to avoid natural salicylates as part of their treatment. See also **aspirin sensitivity**.

Salmonella A genus of bacteria that have given their name to a type of food poisoning known medically as salmonellosis, characterized by abdominal pain, diarrhoea and vomiting. The bacteria can occur in almost any sort of meat and poultry, and in eggs. It may be caught from contaminated kitchens due to unhygienic practices, or by carriers who do not have symptoms of the disorder, or by the use of infected animal products as food for other animals.

salt (also called **common salt**; **sodium chloride**; **table salt**) A mineral that has been used throughout history as a condiment to bring out the flavour of savoury foods. It is also used to preserve foods, either by packing them in salt crystals or pickling them in brine. Salt occurs as underground deposits (**rock salt**) and in sea water (**sea salt**), from which it is extracted. It is the principal source of **sodium** in the diet. People with high blood pressure can benefit from a diet low in salt, but it is not clear if a diet high in salt causes a rise in blood pressure; certainly we eat more salt than our bodies need. To reduce salt intake in the diet cut down on the amount used in cooking and at the table, and eat less processed food with a high salt content.

saltpetre Alternative name for **potassium nitrate**.

salts Any chemical compound formed from the reaction between an **acid** and a **base** or **alkali**. They may also be formed by dissolving a metal in an acid or mixing two other salts together. The salts most commonly used with food are those of calcium, potassium and sodium, particularly as their carbonates or phosphates, or as salts of an **organic acid**. The best-known is common **salt** (sodium chloride).

salvia Alternative name for **sage**.

sauce A seasoned liquid condiment used to flavour, coat or accompany a savoury or sweet dish. Bottled sauces, e.g. Worcester sauce, tomato ketchup and fruit sauces, are really condiments. They usually contain puréed fruit and vegetables in a vinegary syrup, often with added herbs, spices and salt. **Gelling agents**, **preservatives** and **thickeners** may also be included.

savory Any of several labiate plants of the Mediterranean region whose aromatic leaves have a very peppery flavour. They are used as a herb, particularly with bean, egg and tomato dishes.

savoury snack food Any of a variety of non-sweet, usually salty and often spicy food products sold in bags, intended for eating between meals. Savoury snack foods include **crisps**, nuts and products based on puffed corn **starch** or potato starch. Starch-based products are made by extruding or moulding the mixture, frying and then coating it with **flavouring** and **flavour enhancers**. Although many of the additives in savoury snack foods have been removed, or artificial additives replaced with natural ones, these products often still contain **colourings**, flavour enhancers, flavourings and **antioxidants**. They also have high added salt contents, with only a few products providing salt as an optional extra.

scheduled vitamin Any of a number of **vita-**

mins specified in the Labelling of Food Regulations, about which claims can be made. The scheduled vitamins are: vitamin A, thiamin, riboflavin, niacin, folic acid, vitamin B_{12}, vitamin C and vitamin D. Vitamins that are not specified are not allowed to be mentioned on a food product, except in the nutritional information, in the name of the product or in the list of ingredients. Mentioning a vitamin in any other context is taken to be a claim.

sea salt A form of common **salt** (sodium chloride) obtained by evaporating sea water, and usually sold as coarse crystals (unlike free-running table salt). It contains very little iodine, unless added as an ingredient. As with all salt care should be taken not to use too much.

secondary calcium phosphate Alternative name for **calcium hydrogen orthophosphate**.

sell by date A type of datemark, stated in the form of a day and a month on food labels, that indicates the last date on which a product should be sold. It is a statutory requirement on all perishable pre-packed foods that are meant to be eaten within six weeks of packaging. The label should also state the recommended storage conditions and within how many days the food is best eaten by. See also **best before date**; **Food Labelling Regulations**; **use by date**.

sequestrant A substance that has the ability to bind to, and so remove, traces of heavy metals in food (which can cause premature oxidation or setting of gels). The metals, such as copper and iron, usually get into the food with the ingredients or from processing machinery and containers. Chemically, sequestrants are types of **chelating agents**.

sesame seed A sweet, spice seed of an East Indian plant, grown also in other parts of tropical Asia. The seeds may be used as a subtle flavouring for bread and rolls, and in salads and dressing. They also yield a valuable vegetable oil.

shelf life The period of time for which a pre-packed food can remain on sale before its **best before date** or **sell by date** is reached.

shellac (904) A resinous substance produced by scale insects that feed on a species of Indian tree, employed as a **glazing agent**. It can be found on the skins of oranges (and on products made from oranges so treated) and on some cake decorations and sweets.

sherry vinegar A **vinegar** made from sweet sherry and often used with lemon juice in salad dressings.

silica Alternative name for **silicon dioxide**.

silicon dioxide (551; also called **silica)** A common mineral, it is the main component of sand. It is employed as an **anti-caking agent**, **thickener** and **stabilizer**. It is also used as a filter to remove yeast in beer-making.

silver (E174) A precious metal employed to impart a silver colour to dragées and other cake decorations (its only permitted use in the EC). It is banned in the US.

simethicone Alternative name for **dimethylpolysiloxane**.

skin sensitivity An abnormal reaction to skin contact with certain substances, which occurs in susceptible people. See **contact dermatitis**.

slaked lime Alternative name for **calcium hydroxide**.

smoked fish A fish preserved by being dried in wood smoke, a traditional method for cod, haddock, herrings and mackerel. Brown or yellow dyes may be employed to add colour to the fish. Not all fish is produced by the traditional method of smoking, but instead **artificial colours**, e.g. **tartrazine**, **sunset yellow** and **brown FK**, and **flavours** are used. Smoked fish containing **natural colours**, e.g. **annatto** and **crocin**, is also available, while some varieties, such as

Arbroath smokies and Manx kippers, are produced without the use of any additives.

smoke flavour An artificial **flavouring** agent employed to give a smoky flavour to bacon, barbecued meats, ham and smoked fish.

soap clay Alternative name for **bentonite**.

soda bread A type of bread usually made from white flour in which the **raising agent** is **bicarbonate of soda** instead of yeast.

sodium A light, reactive metal needed in the body as part of body fluids and cell contents, and for the proper functioning of nerves. A normal balanced diet contains sufficient sodium for the body's needs. Most dietary sodium is taken in as **salt** (sodium chloride), either as a natural component of foods added during cooking, or at the table or as an ingredient of processed foods. A diet low in salt or sodium is often prescribed for people with high blood pressure (hypertension). Many food additives are sodium compounds (see the following articles).

sodium acetate (262; also called **sodium ethanoate)** The sodium salt of **acetic** (ethanoic) **acid**, employed as an **acidity regulator, buffer** and preservative for liquorice and natural food colours. It may be found in some bread and packet soups.

sodium alginate (E401) A substance made from **alginic acid**, itself extracted from seaweed, widely employed as an **emulsifier**, **gelling agent** and **stabilizer**. It is also used in brewing to precipitate proteins and **tannins**. It may be found in some baked goods, beverages, custard and other desserts, fish and meat products, ice creams and ice lollies, imitation cream, jellies, salad dressings, sauces, soft cheeses and sweets.

sodium aluminosilicate Alternative name for **aluminium sodium silicate**.

sodium aluminium phosphate, acidic (SAP or SALP); sodium aluminium phosphate, basic (KASAL) (541) Synthetic salts made from **orthophosphoric acid**. The acidic formed is employed as a **raising agent** in baked goods, whereas the basic form is an **emulsifier** in cheese-making.

sodium L-ascorbate (E301; also called **sodium L-(+)-ascorbate; vitamin C)** A synthetic form of vitamin C employed as an **antioxidant** and to preserve the colour of foods. It is used mainly in meat products (canned meat, pies and sausages), milk concentrates and baby foods.

sodium benzoate (E211; also called benzoate of soda) The sodium salt of **benzoic acid**, employed as a **preservative** in a wide range of foods including some cheesecake mixes, fruit juices and pies, margarine, pickles, prawns, sauces, soft drinks and sweets. It is also used to preserve other food additives. It is recommended that it should be avoided by people with **aspirin sensitivity**, **asthma** or **urticaria**, and children with a history of **hyperactivity**.

sodium bicarbonate Alternative name for **sodium hydrogen carbonate**.

sodium biphenyl–2-yl oxide (E232; also called dowicide A; natriphene; sodium orthophenyl-phenate; sodium O-phenylphenol) A synthetic **preservative** with a strong soapy smell, used on the skins of citrus fruits or in the paper used to wrap them to prevent them from going mouldy in store. It may be found in jam or marmalade made from fruit so treated.

sodium bisulphite Alternative name for **sodium hydrogen sulphite**.

sodium carbonate (500) An **alkali** and **buffer**, together with **sodium hydrogen carbonate** (sodium bicarbonate) and **sodium sesquicarbonate** (trona), which are included in the designation 500. Sodium hydrogen carbonate is also a **raising agent**, used in many baking powders. These salts may be found in some beer, bread, canned custard, condensed milk and ice cream.

sodium chloride   The chemical name of **salt**.

sodium citrates (E331)   Sodium salts of **citric acid**, including sodium dihydrogen citrate (E331a; also called monosodium citrate), disodium citrate (E331b) and trisodium citrate (E331c). They are versatile additives, employed as **acidity regulators**, **antioxidants**, **buffers**, **emulsifiers**, **sequestrants** and **synergists** for other antioxidants. They are used in a whole range of foods, including canned baby foods, fizzy drinks, ice creams, jams and jellies, margarine, milk products, processed cheese, sweets, vegetable oils and wines.

sodium diacetate   Alternative name for **sodium hydrogen diacetate**.

sodium dihydrogen citrate (E331a)   See **sodium citrates**.

sodium dihydrogen orthophosphate (E339a)   A sodium salt of orthophosphoric acid employed as a **buffer**, **gelling agent**, **stabilizer** and **synergist**. It is also used to clarify sugar. It can be found in some fizzy drinks, instant desserts, meat and meat products and processed cheese.

sodium ethanoate Alternative name for **sodium acetate**.

sodium ethyl para-hydroxybenzoate Alternative name for **ethyl 4-hydroxybenzoate, sodium salt**.

sodium ferrocyanide (535; also called sodium hexacyanoferrate(II)) An inorganic substance employed as an **anti-caking agent** in table salt and as a means of precipitating copper and iron compounds in wine. It is banned in the US.

sodium formate (E237; also called sodium methanoate) The sodium salt of **formic** (methanoic) **acid**, employed as a preservative. It may be found in baked goods, beverages and ice creams. It is not permitted in the UK because there is no technological requirement for it.

sodium gluconate (576) The sodium salt of gluconic acid, employed as a **sequestrant** and yeast food. It is added to sliced apples and some sweets.

sodium guanylate Alternative name for **guanosine 5'-(disodium phosphate)**.

sodium hexacyanoferrate(II) Alternative name for **sodium ferrocyanide**.

sodium hydrogen carbonate (also called **baking soda; sodium bicarbonate**) An acid salt that shares the designation and uses of **sodium carbonate**.

sodium hydrogen diacetate (E262; also called **dykon; sodium diacetate**) A compound of **sodium acetate** (sodium ethanoate) and **acetic acid** (ethanoic acid), employed as an **acidity regulator, preservative** and **sequestrant**. Its fungicidal properties are used against the moulds that can cause sticky yellow patches in bread. Its vinegary smell and taste are put to use in salt and vinegar flavoured crisps.

sodium hydrogen L-glutamate Alternative name for **monosodium glutamate (MSG)**.

sodium hydrogen malate (350) A sodium salt of **malic acid**, employed as a **buffer** and **humectant**, and for its apple flavour. It may be found in canned apples and tomatoes, frozen vegetables, jams, potato snacks, soft drinks, soups and wines.

sodium hydrogen sulphite (E222; also called **acid sodium sulphite; sodium bisulphite**) An inorganic salt employed as a **preservative**, particularly for beer, cider, wine and other alcoholic drinks. It may also be used to whiten fish and sugar. It is used in desserts, frozen chips, frozen shellfish, fruit juices, milk products, powdered potato and sauces. Treating foods with sulphites reduces the thiamin (vitamin B$_1$) content. Sodium hydrogen sulphite should be strictly avoided by people with skin or **food allergies**, **asthma** and kidney or liver disorders. It is not recommended for children with a history of **hyperactivity**.

sodium hydroxide (524; also called caustic soda; lye) An **alkali** employed in making caramel, food oils and malt. It may also be used to adjust the composition of the water supply at a brewery. It can be found in beer, black olives, canned vegetables, cocoa products and jams.

sodium 5'-inosinate Alternative name for **inosine 5'-(disodium phosphate)**.

sodium lactate (E325) The sodium salt of lactic acid, employed as a **bulking agent**, **humectant** and **synergist**. It is used in cheeses, jams and jellies, low-fat spreads, soups and sweets.

sodium malate (350) A sodium salt of **malic acid**, employed as a **buffer** and **flavouring**. It can be found in some jams, jellies and marmalade.

sodium metabisulphite (E223; also called disodium pyrosulphite) A synthetic **antioxidant**, **bleaching agent** and **preservative**. It is used to arrest fermentation in brewing and wine-making. It can be found in beer, cider and wine, desserts and toppings, dried and frozen vegetables, fruit juices, frozen chips and shellfish, milk products, pickles and potato products. It should be strictly avoided by people with **asthma** or **food aversion**, and it is not recommended for children with a history of **hyperactivity**.

sodium methanoate Alternative name for **sodium formate**.

sodium methyl para-hydroxybenzoate Alternative name for **methyl 4-hydroxybenzoate, sodium salt**.

sodium nitrate (E251; also called **Chile saltpetre)** An important **preservative** for meat and meat products, including canned, cured and pressed meats and sausages, in which it combats botulism. It is also used in some cheeses and fish, and for fixing the colours of foods. In the body it is converted to sodium nitrite (see **nitrates and nitrites**). It should not be used in foods intended for babies and young children.

sodium nitrite (E250) A curing agent and **preservative** for smoked fish, meat and nearly all meat products (including patés and sausages), in which it is effective against botulism. It should not be used in foods intended for babies and young children. See **nitrates and nitrites**.

sodium orthophenylphenate Alternative name for **sodium biphenyl–2-yl oxide**.

sodium polyphosphates (E450c) Synthetic salts with the same properties and uses as **potassium polyphosphates**, whose designation E450c they share.

sodium potassium tartrate Alternative name for **potassium sodium L-(+)-tartrate**.

sodium propionate (E281; also called **sodium propanate**) The sodium salt of **propionic** (propanoic) **acid**, employed as a **preservative**, particularly against the moulds that can cause sticky yellow patches in bread dough. It can therefore be found in bread and other baked goods, as well as in dairy products such as processed cheese.

sodium propyl para-hydroxybenzoate Alternative name for **propyl 4-hydroxybenzoate**.

sodium 5′-ribonucleotide (E635) Mixtures of sodium guanylate and sodium 5′-inosinate, employed as **flavour enhancers** in packet soups and potato products. It cannot be used in foods intended for babies and young children, and it should be avoided by people suffering from gout. It is banned in the US.

sodium saccharin The sodium salt of **saccharin**, favoured because it is much more soluble than the parent compound.

sodium salts of fatty acids (E470) Chemically these substances are soaps, employed in the food industry as **anti-caking agents**, **emulsifiers** and **stabilizers**. They can be found in some cake mixes, icing sugar, potato snacks and soup mixes.

sodium sesquicarbonate See **sodium carbonate**.

sodium sorbate (E201) The sodium salt of **sorbic acid**, widely employed as a **preservative** in baked goods, cheese products, dried fruit, margarines and soft drinks.

sodium stearoyl–2–lactylate (E481) A synthetic **emulsifier** and **stabilizer** made from **lactic acid**. It is also used for conditioning bread dough. It can be found in baked goods, cooking fat, icings, milk substitutes, potato snacks, vegetable oils and whipped toppings. It is banned in the US.

sodium sulphate (514; also called Glauber's salt) A naturally occurring mineral salt used as a laxative and employed in brewing to compensate for variations in the local water supply. It may also be used to dilute other food additives. It can be found in some beers and chewing gum.

sodium sulphite (E221) A synthetic salt used as a **preservative** and to sterilize food processing equipment, particularly in brewing and winemaking. It is also an **anti-browning agent** for cut fruits and potatoes. Added to bread dough and biscuit batters it greatly reduces the time the mix has to be left before cooking. It is also used in one of the processes for making caramel. It can be found in beer, frozen chips and shellfish, fruit pie fillings, some fruit juices, powdered eggs and wine. Sodium sulphite should be strictly avoided by people who suffer from **asthma** or allergies (in whom it may trigger an attack of **angioedema** or **urticaria**). It is not recommended for people with kidney or liver disorders, or children with a history of **hyperactivity**.

sodium L-(+)-tartrate Alternative name for **monosodium L-(+)-tartrate** and **disodium L-(+)-tartrate**.

sodium tripolyphosphate Alternative name for **pentasodium triphosphate**.

soft drink A non-alcohol drink available ready-to-drink or in concentrated form requiring dilution. Soft drinks include squash, fruit drinks and carbonated (fizzy) drinks. There are specific requirements for minimum amounts of certain ingredients, e.g. sugar and fruit, in different types of soft drink. Soft drinks are permitted to contain a variety of additives including **preservatives**, **colouring**, **flavourings**, **emulsifiers**, **acids** and other **miscellaneous additives**.

solvent ether Alternative name for **ethyl ether**.

solvent A liquid that dissolves a solid substance – for example, water is a solvent for salt and sugar. (A liquid that dissolves another liquid is usually called a **diluent**.) In the food industry solvents are used to extract substances: flavours may be extracted from fruits or **caffeine** from coffee using **ethyl alcohol** (ethanol) as a solvent. Other solvents include higher alcohols, **glycerol** and its esters, and chlorinated hydrocarbons.

Solvents in Food Regulations A set of regulations issued by the Ministry of Agriculture, Fisheries and Food that control the use of **solvents** in food. The regulations list the carrier solvents that are permitted.

sorbic acid (E200) An organic **acid** that occurs in some fruits and mountain ash berries, but is usually made synthetically for the food industry, in which it is widely employed as a **preservative** against moulds and yeast. Because it is effective in a slightly acid environment, it is particularly valuable in cheese-making and wine-making. Sorbic acid can be found in many foods, including some baked goods, bottled sauces, cheese products, chocolate products, cider, desserts, dried fruits, fruit yoghurts, soft drinks, sweets and wine.

sorbitan monolaurate (493; also called **span 20)** A synthetic **anti-foaming agent, emulsifier** and **stabilizer**. It is used to prevent boiled sugary liquids from frothing, and can be found in jam and boiled sweets.

sorbitan mono-oleate (494; also called **span 80)** A synthetic **emulsifier** and **stabilizer** used in some cake mixes and chewing gum.

sorbitan monopalmitate (495; also called **span 40)** A synthetic **emulsifier** and **stabilizer**, also used as a flavour dispersant. It can be found in some cake mixes and chocolate products.

sorbitan monostearate (491) A synthetic **emulsifier, glazing agent** and **stabilizer**. It is used in cakes, cake mixes, margarines, milk substitutes, whipped toppings and yeast powder.

sorbitan tristearate (492; also called span 65) A synthetic **emulsifer** and **stabilizer**, used in cake mixes, chocolate products, soft drinks and sweets.

sorbitol (E420i) A type of sugar that occurs in various berry fruits, mountain ash berries and seaweed, usually made commercially by the hydrogenation of **glucose**. Its solution is known as sorbitol syrup (E420ii). The sugar and its syrup are employed as **sweeteners** and as a **humectant** and **stabilizer**, and to preserve the texture of toffee and other chewy sweets. They are also used as a substitute for **glycerol** and to mask the bitter aftertaste of **saccharin**.

Sorbitol is absorbed into the body after digestion and converted to the blood sugar glucose, but it is absorbed only slowly and so is a good substitute for sucrose or glucose in foods intended for people with **diabetes**. It has a slight laxative effect and for this reason is not allowed in foods intended for babies and young children. It can be found in desserts, ice cream, pre-packed cakes and pastries, raisins, soft drinks and sweets.

sorbitol syrup (E420ii) A concentrated solution of **sorbitol**.

sorrel A plant that grows in Eurasia and North America whose sour-tasting leaves are used in salads and savoury sauces.

soup Any of a variety of liquid dishes, from consommés to thick broths. The ingredients of canned soups are specified by a code of practice, a set of standards laid down by the manufacturers not the law. It ensures the amounts and quality of the ingredients. For example, meat soups must contain a minimum of 6% meat and a mixed vegetable soup should be made with a minimum of four different vegetables. Canned vegetables may contain a variety of additives including **emulsifiers**, **stabilizers**, **colouring**, **flavour enhancers**, **modified starch**, **sweeteners**, **salt** and **sugar**. Dehydrated soups are not controlled by a code of practice and they tend to contain even more additives including **preservatives** and **antioxidants**.

soured cream A single cream with a fat content of 18%, which has had natural bacterial agents, **rennet** or acid (e.g. **lactic** or **acetic acid**) added to bring about souring.

span 20 Alternative name for **sorbitan monolaurate**.

span 40 Alternative name for **sorbitan monoplamitate**.

span 65 Alternative name for **sorbitan tristearate**.

span 80 Alternative name for **sorbitan mono-oleate**.

spermaceti (also called **sperm oil**) A thin, yellow liquid obtained from the sperm whale. It is used as a **release agent** in baking tins, and can sometimes be found in baked goods.

sperm oil Alternative name for **spermaceti**.

spice An aromatic flavouring usually made from the dried flower-heads, roots or seeds of various plants and used in savoury and sweet dishes.

spirit A vague term usually denoting **ethyl alcohol** (ethanol) or an **alcoholic drink** or **solution**.

spirit vinegar See **vinegar**.

stabilizer A substance that is added to an **emulsion** to prevent it from separating out. It may also act as a **gelling agent** and **thickener**, and serve to prevent a foam or froth from collapsing. Often the substance that causes an emulsion to form, an **emulsifier**, is also a stabilizer.

star anise A star-shaped, highly flavoured spice made from the whole dried seed pods of the **aniseed** plant, used particularly in meat dishes.

starch A **carbohydrate** substance found in all plants, particularly in seeds (where it acts as a food supply for the germinating embryo) and energy-storage organs such as rhizomes, tubers and swollen roots. Chemically it is a **polysaccharide**, a polymer of the sugar **glucose**, which can be made from it by treatment with acids or alkalis (**hydrolysis**). It is a principal food in the human diet, provided chiefly by cereals and potatoes; it is also a principal source of calories, being converted into the blood sugar glucose after digestion. Natural starch can be modified in various ways for use in the food industry. See **modified starch**.

stearic acid (570; also called **octadecanoic acid)** An organic **acid** prepared from fats and oils and used as an **anti-caking agent**. It can be found in chewing gum and sweets.

stearyl tartrate (E483) A synthetic substance made from tartaric acid, employed as an **emulsifier, flour treatment agent** and **stabilizer**. It can be found in baked goods and cake mixes.

sterculia gum Alternative name for **karaya gum**.

sterilization Any method of destroying or removing disease-causing organisms in a food or other substance. There are several methods including **pasteurization**, **ultra heat treated (UHT)**, **preservatives** and **food irradiation**.

stock cube A ready-made stock preparation in the form of cubes. They can be used to make stock quickly for soups, sauces and stews or casseroles. Stock cubes are available in a variety of flavours including beef, chicken and vegetable. Most contain both salt and **flavour enhancers**, which contribute to the high **sodium** content. This should be appreciated when adding any further seasoning to the dish. Stock cubes that contain no additives are also available, particularly the vegetable varieties.

stomach cramp Pain caused by contraction of the abdominal muscles, itself resulting from overexertion or possibly a **gastric upset**. It may accompany nausea.

storage conditions The way a pre-packed food should be stored – for instance in a dry place or in a refrigerator or freezer – has to be stated on the label along with the **best before date** or **sell by date**. See **Food Labelling Regulations**.

succinic acid (363) An organic **acid** that occurs naturally in broccoli and beets but is manufactured from acetic acid for use as an

acidity regulator and **buffer**. It can be found in some baked goods and breakfast cereals.

sucroglycerides (E474) Synthetic **emulsifiers** and **stabilizers**, used in cakes, crisps, dessert mixes and margarines.

sucrose The chemical name for table **sugar**, as made from sugar-cane or sugar-beet.

sucrose esters of fatty acids (E473) Synthetic **emulsifiers** and **stabilizers**, used in cakes, dessert mixes and margarines.

sugar Table sugar made from cane-sugar or beet-sugar, known chemically as sucrose, is the commonest **sweetener**. There are also various other natural sugars, such as **glucose** (dextrose), **fructose**, **maltose** and **lactose**. Sucrose contributes to the development of tooth decay and may also lead to excessive energy intake (calories) and overweight. For these reasons, it is sometimes partly or completely replaced by **artificial sweeteners**.

sulphur dioxide (E220) A poisonous choking gas widely employed as a disinfectant, **anti-browning agent** for cut fruit, **antioxidant** for fats and oils, **bleaching agent** for flour, and general all-round **preservative** and fungicide (particularly in wine-making). It is commonly used to prevent stored fruits from going mouldy. It is also used in malting barley to retain as much sugar as possible in the malt. There are few types of foods in which sulphur dioxide (or its related salts, sulphites) cannot be found. This makes it difficult for people with **asthma** or kidney or liver disorders to avoid it. It is also not recommended for children with a history of **hyperactivity**.

The long list of products that may contain sulphur dioxide includes alcoholic drinks; desserts, drinks, fillings, ice lollies, jams, jellies, juices and syrups containing fruits; and dried or dehydrated fruits, nuts, soups, spices and vegetables.

sulphuric acid (513) A mineral **acid** employed in brewing to retain sugars in malt and to adjust the acidity of the water supply, and in the production of **modified starch**. It can be found in some beers.

summer savory An aromatic herb with a pleasant bitter taste and a scent rather like thyme. It is used particularly with other herbs in stuffings for poultry and veal.

sunset yellow FCF (E110) A synthetic **azo dye** and **coal tar dye** employed in wide range of foods to impart an orange or yellow colour to them. It is used in some baked goods, breadcrumbs, breakfast cereals, cheese sauce mixes, fish fingers, ice creams, lemon curd, marmalades, marzipan, orange jellies and drinks, pickles and powdered desserts. It should be avoided by people with **aspirin sensitivity**, **asthma** or other allergic conditions, and by children with a history of **hyperactivity**. It is banned in Finland, Norway and Portugal.

suspension A mixture in which an insoluble solid is incorporated with a liquid, for instance a finely divided chalk or china clay in water. If left to stand, a suspension eventually separates out with the solid component underneath the liquid one.

sweet cicely (also called **myrrh**) An umbelliferous plant native to Europe whose aromatic leaves, which taste like aniseed, are sometimes used as a savoury flavouring in salad dressings and soups.

sweetener Any substance, natural or artificial, that adds a sweet flavour to food. Most natural sweeteners are **sugars** or related carbohydrate compounds, sometimes replaced in manufactured foods for cost or dietary reasons by **artificial sweeteners**. In the terms of the **Sweeteners in Food Regulations (1983)**, a sweetener is restricted to non-carbohydrate substances, i.e. **mannitol**, **sorbitol**, sorbitol syrup and the artificial sweeteners.

Sweeteners in Food Regulations (1983) A set of regulations issued by the Ministry of Agriculture, Fisheries and Food that specify the **sweeteners** permitted in food.

sweet woodruff A plant that grows in Asia, Europe and northern Africa. Although sweet woodruff is not usually used in cooking it is an important flavouring in the German wine Maibowle, which is traditionally served on 1st May. It is also used in punches and fruit cups.

synergist A substance that, added to another, produces an action that is significantly greater than the predicted combined action of the two. In the food industry, most synergists increase the effectiveness of **antioxidants**. The commonest are the salts of **citric** and **tartaric acids** (and the acids themselves).

synthetic A synonym for artificial, man-made or non-natural. Thus a synthetic substance is one that is made from other starting materials in a laboratory. However, it is possible to synthesize substances that are chemically identical to their natural versions. For example, **ascorbic acid** (vitamin C) has exactly the same taste and physiological effects on the body whether it is eaten as a component of pure natural lemon juice or in a synthesized form when added to a food or vitamin tablet. Such

236

synthetic substances are sometimes described as nature identical.

synthetic alpha-tocopherol See **alpha-tocopherol, synthetic**.

synthetic delta-tocopherol See **delta-tocopherol, synthetic**.

synthetic gamma-tocopherol See **gamma-tocopherol, synthetic**.

syrup A usually viscous, concentrated solution of a **sugar**.

Tabasco A very hot thin sauce made from fermented, powdered dried fruits of chilli peppers (capsicums) and mixed with spirit, vinegar and salt. A traditional sauce with Mexican dishes.

table salt See **salt**.

talc (553b; also called French chalk; magnesium hydrogen metasilicate) A naturally occurring mineral employed as an **anti-caking agent**, filter medium and **release agent**, also used as a coating on foods to stop them from sticking together. It can be found in some chewing gum, icing sugar and packet noodles.

tamarind An evergreen tropical tree whose brown pulpy seed pods are used as a spice. It is sold dried and then soaked in warm water to make a juice, which is commonly added to chutneys, curries and sauces to give a sour flavour. The pulp is also a source of **tartaric acid**.

tannic acid (also called **tannin**) A bitter-tasting substance that occurs in the bark and unripe fruits of various trees and in oak galls, as well as in cocoa, coffee, tea and red wines. It is used traditionally to tan leather, and in beer- and wine-making to precipitate proteins. In the food industry it may be added to baked goods, caramel, ices and sweets.

tannin Alternative name for **tannic acid**.

tansy A plant whose aromatic leaves are used as a flavouring.

tarragon A Eurasian plant whose aromatic leaves are used as a herb and seasoning.

L-(+)-tartaric acid (E334) An organic substance with a strongly acidic taste that occurs in various fruits (particularly tamarind fruit) and in wine, which is the chief commercial source. It is employed as an **acidity regulator**, **antioxidant** and **synergist** for other antioxidants, and as the acid component (with a **raising agent**) in some baking powders. It is used in some canned fruits and vegetables, dried eggs, fizzy drinks, frozen milk products, and jams and jellies.

tartaric acid esters of mono- and diglycerides of fatty acids (E472d) Synthetic substances made from **tartaric acid**, employed as **emulsifiers** and **stabilizers**. They are used in cheesecake mixes, cooking fats, crisps, gravy powder, margarines and soups.

tartrazine (E102) An **azo dye** used as a **colouring** agent to impart a yellow colour to foods, which has achieved some notoriety because of its association with **hyperactivity** in children. It has also caused allergic reactions in other sensitive people. Tartrazine can be mixed with other synthetic colours to make cream, orange or green shades.

Tartrazine is widely used in a whole range of foods: boiled sweets, bottled sauces, cake mixes, canned vegetables, custard powder, desserts, ice lollies, icings, instant puddings, jams and jellies, marzipan, pickles, ready-made mustard, salad dressing, smoked fish and soft drinks. It should be avoided by people with **aspirin sensitivity**, **asthma** or **urticaria**. It is banned in Finland and Norway, and its use is restricted in a few other European countries, although not in the UK.

tea An evergreen shrub related to camellia which is grown throughout tropical Asia for its leaves, which are dried and used to make a beverage by adding boiling water. Tea contains

caffeine and **tannic acid**, although **decaffeinated** varieties are available.

tenderizer A substance added to meat to break down the **protein** in muscle and make it more tender after cooking. Natural **enzymes** carry out this process if meat is left to hang, but commercially it is hastened by adding enzyme concentrates, such as proteases, papain and trypsin.

tetrapotassium diphosphate (E450a) A potassium salt of pyrophosphoric acid, employed as a **buffer**, **emulsifier**, **sequestrant** and **stabilizer**. It can be found in some breakfast cereals, cheese spreads, condensed milk, cream, frozen chickens and processed meats.

tetrasodium diphosphate (E450a; also called tetrasodium pyrophosphate) A sodium salt of pyrophosphoric acid whose properties and uses are the same as those of **tetrapotassium diphosphate**, and shares the designation E450a.

tetrasodium pyrophosphate Alternative name for **tetrasodium diphosphate**.

texture modifier Any substance that alters the 'feel' of a food in the mouth, from natural substances such as gelatin and starch to synthetic **firming agents**, **gelling agents** and **thickeners**.

thaumatin A natural **sweetener** and **flavour enhancer** extracted from an African fruit. It is a **protein** and the sweetest substance yet discovered. It has a slight laxative effect and is not permitted in foods intended for babies and young children.

thiaben Alternative name for **2-(thiazol–4-yl) benzimidazole**.

thiabendazole Alternative name for **2-(thiazol–4-yl) benzimidazole**.

thiamin (also called **thiamine**; **vitamin B₁**) A member of the vitamin B complex. It is needed in the body for growth, the release of energy from food and to help with the proper functioning of the heart and nervous system. Foods rich in thiamin include whole-grain cereals, meat (particularly pork, liver and kidney), pulses (peas and beans) and nuts. Deficiency of the vitamin causes beriberi. The use of **sulphur dioxide** or sulphites as preservatives in foods reduces their thiamin content.

2-(thiazol–4-yl) benzimidazole (E233; also called **omnizole**; **thiaben**; **thiabendazole**; **tribenzole**) A synthetic **preservative**, a fungicide that is applied to the skins of fruits and some vegetables to stop them from going mouldy. It can be found on apples, bananas, citrus fruits, grapes, pears and tomatoes. It is banned (except as a pesticide in farming) in the United States.

thickener A substance added to a liquid food to increase its viscosity. Many thickeners are also **gelling agents**. They include a wide range of natural vegetable products – many based on **agar**, **alginic acid**, cellulose, plant gums or starch – and the mineral **silicon dioxide** (silica).

thyme A small labiate shrub of northern temperate regions whose aromatic leaves are used, fresh or dried, as a herb in bouquet garni, meat dishes and stuffings.

tin A metallic element used to coat steel cans for containing preserved foods. Any tendency for the tin to contaminate the food (e.g. if the food is acidic) is prevented by lacquering the inside of the can or adding a **sequestrant** to the food. For drinks, tin cans have been largely superseded by ones made of **aluminium**.

titanium dioxide (E171) A naturally-occurring mineral employed as a whitener and to increase the opacity of creams and sauces. It can be found in some soft cheeses, horseradish cream and sauce, lemon curd and sweets, and as a surface coating on biscuits and ices. It is banned in Germany, Japan, Portugal and Spain.

tocopherols, in extracts of natural origin (E306; also called **vitamin E)** A natural form of vitamin E employed as an **antioxidant**, extracted from various vegetable sources such as cottonseed, green leaves, maize (sweetcorn), rice germ, soya bean oil and wheat germ. It can be found in some dessert toppings, meat pies and vegetable fats and oils.

toxin A poisonous substance, usually one that is produced by a microorganism, such as botulin the toxin that causes **botulism**.

trace elements Minerals necessary in the diet in very small quantities in order to maintain good health. Nine trace elements are at present known to be essential to humans: chromium, copper, cobalt, iodine, magnesium, manganese, molybdenum, selenium and zinc. They are usually distinguished from the minerals calcium, iron, phosphorus, potassium, sodium and chlorine (sometimes known as essential elements), which are needed in larger quantities. A normal balanced diet contains sufficient trace elements for the body's needs.

tragacanth (E413; also called **gum dragon**; **gum tragacanth)** A natural gum obtained from thorny shrubs of the pea family that grow in the Middle East. It is employed as an **emulsifier**, **stabilizer** and **thickener**, and to prevent the sugar in sweets from crystallizing. It is used in bottled sauces, cottage, cream and processed cheeses, ice lollies, jams and jellies, piccalilli, salad dressing, sweets and yoghurt.

triacetin Alternative name for **glycerol triacetate**.

triammonium citrate (380; also called **ammonium citrate tribasic**; **citric acid triammonium salt**) An ammonium salt of **citric acid**, employed as a **buffer** and **emulsifier**. It can be found in various cheese spreads and processed cheeses. It is banned in the US.

tribenzole Alternative name for **2-(thiazol–4-yl) benzimidazole**.

tricalcium citrate See **calcium citrate**.

tricalcium diorthophosphate (E341c; also called **calcium phosphate tribasic**; **tricalcium phosphate**) An **anti-caking agent**, **buffer**, **firming agent** and yeast food, also employed to clarify sugar syrups. It can be found in cake mixes, cocoa powder, dried milk, flour, icing sugar, instant drinks, instant soups, powdered sugar, seasoning mixes and table salt.

tricalcium phosphate Alternative name for **tricalcium diorthophosphate**.

triglyceride An **ester** of **glycerol** (propan–1,2,3-triol) in which all three of glycerol's hydroxy groups are replaced by fatty acid residues. Most **fats** and **oils** are triglycerides.

tripotassium citrate (E332; also called **potassium citrate)** A potassium salt of **citric acid**, employed as an **antioxidant**, **buffer**, **emulsifier** and **sequestrant**. It is used in biscuits, crisps, fizzy drinks, dessert toppings, fats and oils, jams and jellies, processed cheeses, processed fruits, sweets and wines.

tripotassium orthophosphate (E340c; also called **dipotassium phosphate**; **DKP**; **potassium phosphate tribasic**; **tripotassium monophosphate)** A potassium salt of **orthophosphoric acid**, employed as a **buffer**, **emulsifier**, **sequestrant** and **synergist**. It is also used as a yeast food. It can be found in some clear soups, cured meats, drinking chocolate, instant custard, powdered milk and wine.

trisodium citrate See **sodium citrates**.

trisodium diphosphate (E450a) A sodium salt of pyrophosphoric acid, employed as a **buffer**, **emulsifier**, **sequestrant** and **stabilizer**. It is also used to improve the colour of meat products. It can be found in some bread, breakfast cereals, condensed milk, frozen chicken and processed cheeses.

trisodium orthophosphate (E339c) A sodium salt of **orthophosphoric acid**, employed

245

as a **buffer**, **sequestrant** and **synergist**. It is used in some cheese products, dessert mixes, fizzy drinks and meat products.

turmeric A yellow condiment and **colouring** made from the powdered dried underground stems of a tropical Asian plant of the ginger family. It has an aromatic, slightly bitter taste and is used sparingly in curries, pickles and relishes. Turmeric is also used to colour rice.

tween 20 Alternative name for **polyoxy-ethylene (20) sorbitan monolaurate**.

tween 40 Alternative name for **polyoxy-ethylene (40) sorbitan monopalmitate**.

tween 60 Alternative name for **polyoxy-ethylene (60) sorbitan monostearate**.

tween 65 Alternative name for **polyoxy-ethylene (65) sorbitan tristearate**.

tween 80 Alternative name for **polyoxy-ethylene (80) sorbitan mono-oleate**.

UHT Abbreviation for **ultra heat treated**.

ultra heat treated (UHT) A method of steri-lizing foods, usually milk, and to extend the shelf life of foods. It involves very high temperatures (130°) over a short period (2 seconds). See also **pasteurization**.

unnumbered additive A large group of additives that are not yet covered by permitted lists. These include **modified starches** and **flavours**. The name of the specific substance does not need to appear on the label, only the general name of 'modified starch' or 'flavourings'. Modified starches are expected to be given **E numbers** in the near future and the EC are trying to produce some form of control for flavours, but with over 4000 different types it is unlikely to be E numbers.

unwrapped food Unlike pre-packed foods, unwrapped foods and other foods sold 'loose' do not have to have labels carrying datemarks, information about ingredients, and so on. See **Food Labelling Regulations**.

urticaria (also called **hives**; **nettle-rash**) A skin reaction characterized by wheals and an itching rash. More serious forms involve raised lumps (see **angioedema**). It can be caused by a **food allergy** or **food intolerance**, and may be treated in the short term with antihistamines. In the long term, the person concerned should avoid the substance causing the reaction.

use by date A datemark on perishable goods

telling the consumer by what day the produce must be eaten. See **sell by date**.

vanilla A tropical climbing plant of the orchid family that bears long pods containing bean-like seeds which are the source of a spice used to flavour sweets and desserts. The pods are sold whole or as the essence extracted from the pod.

vanillin An organic substance that is the active ingredient of **vanilla**. It can be synthesized and used as vanilla flavouring.

vegetables The edible leaves, fruit, roots, flowers or stalks of plants. It is not usually possible to know what pesticides, herbicides or fungicides have been used on fresh vegetables, although it is sometimes possible to find information on the boxes that they are packed in. An alternative, for those concerned about the levels of chemicals in food, is to buy vegetables that have been organically grown. See also **canned vegetables; frozen food**.

vegetable carbon See **carbon black**.

vegetable dye A plant pigment that may be extracted and used to colour food products. Such colours, although less consistent than **artificial colours**, are becoming increasingly popular. They are perceived by the consumer to be 'safer' because they occur naturally in unprocessed foods. There are a variety of vegetable dyes including, **chlorophyll**, **carotenes**, **xanthophylls**, **beetroot red** and **anthocyanins**.

vegetable extract A concentrated flavouring made from vegetable matter, rather than meat or yeast, which is used in small quantities in savoury dishes. Soya sauce is an example of a vegetable extract, it is made from boiled, fermented soya beans. Vegetable extracts may contain added flavouring, **flavour enhancer** and **colouring** and they may also have a high salt content.

vermouth A blended **alcoholic drink** that is made from sweet or dry white, rosé or red wine to which aromatic herbs have been added.

vinegar A condiment and **flavouring** that consists essentially of a 4–6% solution of **acetic acid** (ethanoic acid) in water. Traditionally it is obtained as a by-product of brewing (malt vinegar), cider-making (cider vinegar) or wine-making (wine vinegar). It may be made synthetically from acetic acid, when it is sometimes termed non-brewed condiment (also known as acid, spirit or white vinegar). The synthetic version may have added **colouring** (e.g. caramel). Vinegar is used as a **preservative** and to add flavour to pickles, salad dressings and sauces.

violoxanthin (E161e) A naturally occurring **xanthophyll** plant pigment, obtained from yellow pansies and orange skins. It could be employed as a yellow **colouring** agent, but apparently is not used by the food industry.

vitamin An essential nutrient that is needed by the body in small quantities for growth and to maintain good health. There are some 20 vitamins. The body can make a few vitamins for itself (e.g. vitamin D), but most have to be supplied in food. A normal balanced diet contains a sufficient quantity of all the necessary vitamins, except perhaps at certain stages in life – infancy, pregnancy, old age – or during certain illnesses, when vitamin supplements may be prescribed. A lack of dietary vitamins can cause various deficiency disorders. Many vitamins do not tolerate overcooking or high temperatures, and they are depleted by many methods of food preservation (except for freeze-drying and quick-freezing).

If a claim is to be made that a food is a rich or excellent source of a particular vitamin, the amount of food that could be reasonably expected to be eaten in one day must contain one half of the recommended daily amount (RDA) of that particular vitamin. The claim that a food contains vitamins can only be made if a normal serving of the food contains at least one-sixth of the RDA for those vitamins mentioned on the label. The label must also give the percentage of the RDA that the food provides and the number of servings per pack. See the following articles.

vitamin A A fat-soluble vitamin necessary for healthy skin and mucous membranes, and for good night vision. Foods rich in it include liver, milk and dairy products, butter, margarine, eggs, carrots, green leafy vegetables, dried apricots and tomatoes. By law it must be added to margarine; to match the natural vitamin A content of butter. Deficiency of vitamin A causes dry eyes and skin and night blindness. Excess vitamin A can also be harmful, leading to hair loss and peeling, yellow skin.

vitamin B₁ Alternative name for **thiamin**.

vitamin B₂ Alternative name for **riboflavin**.

vitamin B₆ Alternative name for **pyridoxine**.

vitamin B₁₂ (also called **cyanocobalamin**) A member of the vitamin B complex, needed in the body for growth and the proper formation of red blood cells. Good food sources include liver (and other offal), meat, fish, dairy products and eggs. It is absent in vegetables, which could present a problem to vegans and vegetarians, who may be recommended to taken vitamin B_{12} supplements or foods enriched with the vitamin. Deficiency of the vitamin causes pernicious **anaemia**.

vitamin C Alternative name for **L-ascorbic acid**.

vitamin D (also called **calciferol; cholecalciferol**) A fat-soluble vitamin needed in the body for the proper absorption of calcium and phosphorus, and thus for the formation of healthy bones and teeth. Foods rich in it include fatty fish, margarine, eggs, butter and milk. It is also formed in the body by the action of sunlight on the skin. Deficiency of vitamin D causes rickets in children and osteomalacia in adults.

vitamin E, natural See **tocopherol, in extracts of natural origin**.

vitamin E, synthetic See **alpha-tocopherol**.

vitamin K (also called **phylloquinone**) A vitamin needed by the body for proper blood clotting. Foods rich in it include green leafy vegetables and liver. It is also formed in the intestines by bacterial action. Deficiency of vitamin K causes bleeding (especially in babies).

vomiting A common consequence of **nausea**, which can have an emotional or a physical cause.

water A clear, colourless, tasteless and odourless liquid that is essential for plant and animal life, although not considered a nutrient. Most tap water contains dissolved gases and minerals. Water from chalk and limestone areas is hard and contains chemicals such as bicarbonates, chlorides and sulphates of calcium, **magnesium**, **potassium** and **sodium**.

Tap water is purified by a variety of methods and certain chemicals, e.g. **chlorine** and **calcium oxide**, are added as part of the purification process. Lead can be detected in water which has flowed through lead pipes. **Fluoride** in the drinking water (in concentrations of 1 ppm) is considered by many medical authorities to help prevent dental caries (tooth decay). In most parts of the country fluoride concentrations are between one-tenth and one-fifth of this level and in some areas just above it. Certain water authorities add fluoride to the water supply to bring it up to the level of 1 ppm. The levels of **nitrate** in drinking water are monitored and kept to the levels set by the World Health Organization (WHO).

Water must be included in the list of ingredients when it is more than 5% of the weight of a food product. See also **bottled water**.

wax, refined, microcrystalline (907) A mineral wax obtained from petroleum, employed as polishing agent, **release agent** and as an ingredient of chewing gum. It is banned in the US.

wheatgerm bread A type of bread made from either brown or white **flour** that has 10% or more wheatgerm added to the dough.

whipped cream A cream that must have a minimum fat content of 35% by law and which is sold ready-whipped. Whipped cream is permitted to contain **emulsifiers** and **stabilizers** and these must be declared on the label. See also **aerosol cream**.

whipping cream A cream that must have a minimum fat content of 35% by law and which has not been homogenized, therefore making it suitable for whipping. When whipped correctly this cream should double in volume, unwhipped it can be used for pouring. It contains no additives.

white bread A bread that is made with white **flour**. Traditionally **bleaching agents** have been used to whiten the otherwise yellow-grey flour, but this practice is now less common. **Improving agents** such as **ascorbic acid** are used to strengthen the **gluten** to assist in producing a good-quality loaf. **Preservatives, emulsifiers, raising agents** and **acids** are also permitted (see **flour improving agents**). Yeast nutrients, e.g. **ammonium chloride** and **calcium sulphate**, may be employed to encourage yeast growth. White flour is fortified with **iron, calcium, thiamin** and **nicotinic acid**.

white peppercorn   A hot condiment made from the dried ripe seeds of the pepper plant. See also **black peppercorn; green peppercorn; pepper**.

wholemeal bread   A bread that is made with **wholemeal flour**. It is permitted to contain a variety of additives including **colouring (caramel), preservatives, acids, emulsifiers, yeast nutrients, raising agents** and **improving agents**, but many wholemeal breads are now completely free from additives.

wholemeal flour   A **flour** that contains 100% of the wheat grain and is therefore made up of starchy endosperm, bran and germ. Under the **Bread and Flour Regulations** wholemeal flour is not permitted to contain additives except colour as **caramel** and some **enzymes**.

Stoneground flour is milled in the traditional way between two millstones to produce a coarser, textured flour than that produced by roller milling. Strong, plain and self-raising types of flour are all widely available.

wine An **alcoholic drink** made by fermenting (using yeast) the sugars in various fruit juices, particularly grape juice. In commercial wine-making, additives are employed at various stages in the manufacturing process. But because wines almost invariably contain more than 1.2% alcohol, they are exempt from **Food Labelling Regulations**. Although drinks with such an alcoholic strength are exempt from carrying a list of ingredients this certainly does not mean that they contain no additives.

Sulphur dioxide is commonly used as a preservative in wine, an additive that **asthma** sufferers are particularly susceptible to. Aeration of wine is achieved by the use of **carbon dioxide** and **yeast nutrients** are also permitted. A variety of **processing aids** may be used to clarify the wine after fermentation, e.g. edible **gelatin**, **isinglass**, casein, **albumin**, **bentonite**, **silicon dioxide**, **kaolin**, **tannin** and pectinolytic enzymes. Many of these are of animal origin, which would be unacceptable to certain vegetarians and religious groups. **Sorbic acid** is permitted to inhibit the growth of moulds and yeasts, and **acids** and **alkalis** are used to achieve the correct environmental conditions for wine making.

wine vinegar   A type of **vinegar** produced as a by-product of wine-making.

woodruff   A Eurasian plant whose fragrant leaves are used as herbs to flavour wines and liqueurs.

Worcester sauce (also called Worcestershire sauce)   A type of savoury bottled **sauce** consisting mainly of soy sauce, vinegar and spices.

xanthan gum (E415; also called corn sugar gum)   A synthetic gum made by the fermentation of corn (maize) syrup, employed as an **emulsifier**, **stabilizer** and **thickener**. It is also used as a substitute for **gluten** in foods for people who cannot tolerate this protein. It can be found in cake mixes, dairy products, ice cream, instant desserts, salad dressings, sauces and toppings.

xanthophylls (E161)   A group of mostly yellow plant pigments related to **carotenes**, found in green leaves and yellow or orange flowers, fruits and vegetables. They are widely used as food colouring agents and include (among those allocated E numbers) **canthaxanthin**, **crysptoxanthin**, **flavoxanthin**, **lutein**, **rhodoxanthin**, **rubixanthin** and **violoxanthin**.

257

xylitol A natural plant product employed as a **humectant** and **sweetener**. It has about the same sweetness as the less expensive sucrose, and is used in some chewing gums, jams, ice creams and sweets. It is not permitted in foods intended for babies and young children.

yeast A member of a group of microscopic (single-celled) fungi, employed in bread-making, brewing, wine-making and various other processes that involve fermentation. Yeast is also a good source of **vitamins**, particularly those of the vitamin B complex.

yeast extract A concentrated **flavouring** made by the action of acid on yeast. Yeast extracts are used to flavour savoury foods such as soups, stews and casseroles. They can also be used as a sandwich spread or to make a hot savoury drink. Although rich in B vitamins they also have high salt contents and may also contain added flavouring.

yeast nutrient A substance added to **yeast** to enable it to multiply in various fermentation processes, particularly brewing and wine-making. Such nutrients include phosphates and ammonium, calcium and potassium salts.

yellow 2G (107; also called **acid yellow 17**; **food yellow 5**) An **azo dye** and **coal tar dye**

similar to **tartrazine**, once employed as a yellow colouring agent in foods. It has now been banned throughout the EC and the US.

yoghurt A creamy dessert made by the fermentation of milk using bacteria. It often contains added **sweeteners** (natural or artificial), chocolate or fruit (or **flavourings** that imitate them), **emulsifiers**, **stabilizers** and **thickeners**. **Preservatives** are permitted in fruit yoghurt, or in the fruit used to make them.

zest Thinly sliced lemon or orange peel, which contains essential oils and is employed as an acidic fruity flavouring. It should be remembered that the skins of citrus fruits are often treated with fungicides and polishing agents, and may be labelled with synthetic dyes.

Appendix I

Additive-Free Shopping

The Label

Today's shopper is confronted by a great variety of food and drink, in a wide range of different forms. This means that it is vitally important to understand the information provided on the product label to ensure that a wise and healthy choice is made. Since the introduction of the Food Labelling Regulations in 1984, far more information is now required by law to be stated on the label.

For most products the following information must be given:

1. The name or description of the food.
2. A list of ingredients.
3. How long it keeps and under what conditions.
4. Its weight, volume or number of items in the pack.
5. The name and address of the manufacturer, packer or seller.
6. The place of origin, if omitting this information could be considered misleading to the customer.
7. Instructions for use, if omitting this information could make it difficult to use the product properly.

In addition, labels are increasingly providing

261

nutritional information, although this is not yet a legal requirement. Some product labels may claim particular benefits for a food, for example that the food is suitable for certain people, or that it is high in fibre or low in fat.

There are a few foods that are not required to comply with the Food Labelling Regulations because they have their own special regulations. These include certain sugar products, cocoa and chocolate products, honey, condensed and dried milk and cheese.

The Name

A food may have a prescribed name which is covered by a legal definition in food regulations, e.g. 'yoghurt' or 'wholemeal bread'. Other foods have a customary or traditional name that is not defined by law, but is known by most people, e.g. 'muesli' or 'pizza'.

New foods or unfamiliar foods must have a descriptive name so that they can be distinguished from other products, e.g. 'malted milk drink' or 'sage and onion stuffing'. Trade, brand or fancy names cannot be used alone, but must have a description as well. 'Soufflé Napolitana' does not describe what the food is at all, but 'cheese soufflé with spaghetti and tomato filling' leaves the customer in no doubt. The name must also indicate any processing that the food has undergone, e.g. 'smoked bacon', 'frozen peas' or 'dried raisins'.

A name that might mislead the consumer is not allowed. For example, raspberry yoghurt can only be called 'raspberry yoghurt', or 'raspberry flavoured yoghurt', or show raspberries on the pot if the flavouring comes mainly from real raspberries. If the flavour comes mainly or completely from an added flavouring it must be called 'raspberry flavour yoghurt'. 'Vanilla essence' must be obtained from vanilla pods, but 'vanilla flavouring' can be totally synthetic.

The Ingredients

The labels on most pre-packed foods must give a full list of ingredients. The exceptions are:

1. Fresh fruit and vegetables that are not cut into pieces.
2. Carbonated water that has only carbon dioxide added to it.
3. Vinegar that has nothing added to it.
4. Most cheeses, butter, fermented milks and flavourings.
5. Alcoholic drinks that have an alcoholic content of more than 1.2% by volume.
6. Foods that consist of a single ingredient.

Some foods need only give a name and the categories of any additives. These include unwrapped foods, food made and wrapped on the premises and baked goods in crimped cases or transparent wrapping. Unwrapped bread, cakes, pastries and meat need no label at all if there is any sign or label close-by declaring any additives that are used. Many butchers have notices in their shops stating that artificial colour and preservatives are used in their sausages.

Ingredients must be declared in descending order of weight. The amount of ingredients used in the preparation of the food is taken as the weight of the ingredient for the purposes of the label, with the exception of water. Water is considered as an ingredient, but its position in the list depends on the amount of water in the final product. It is not declared in the following instances: if it is used to reconstitute dried or concentrated ingredients; if it is not normally consumed, e.g. brine in canned vegetables; if its weight is 5% or less of the finished product.

Compound ingredients such as pasta in lasagne have to be given in the ingredient list in one of two ways. First, each individual ingredient of the pasta can be listed in the appropriate position for its weight. Second, the pasta can be listed in the appropriate position for the total weight of pasta, with a list of all its ingredients next to it in brackets. If an ingredient is given a special emphasis, e.g. 'with extra fruit', the minimum amount of that ingredient, as a percentage of the total weight, must appear close to the name or in the relevant place in the ingredient list. The names of some ingredients are covered by law. For example, it is not permitted to simply state 'fat', it must be qualified by stating whether it is animal or vegetable fat.

The ingredient list must also declare any additives that have been added as ingredients. An additive may be listed either by its category name followed by its specific name, e.g. Preservative: sorbic acid, or its category name followed by its permitted number, e.g. Preservative: E200. The category of flavours is an exception because all flavours are covered by the single entry 'flavourings'. An additive may already be present in an ingredient that is then used in another food product, e.g. sulphite added to fruit which is then used to make jam. Some sulphite might be present in the final product, but it does not have to be declared if the amount carried over is too small to have a preservative effect on the jam. Additives that are used solely as processing aids are not usually declared either, only if their function continues in the final product, e.g. anti-caking agents in salt or icing sugar. Flour is considered a single food and therefore the additives present in flour are not declared on bread labels, as long as the additives used are permitted in the Bread and Flour Regulations.

The Datemark
Most foods must carry a datemark. The exceptions are:
1. Foods that are not pre-packed.
2. Foods with a shelf life of more than 18

months.

3. Eggs.

4. Very long-life foods, e.g. vinegar, sugar and cooking salt.

5. Cheese that is intended to ripen after it is packed.

6. Most alcoholic drinks.

7. Fresh fruit and vegetables that are not peeled or cut.

8. Frozen foods and ice cream that carry a star marking.

9. Flour confectionery and bread that is intended to be eaten within 24 hours.

The type of datemark used depends on the expected shelf life of the product. Products that have a shelf life of less than 6 weeks carry a 'sell by date', with the date in days and months. There should also be an indication of when the product should be eaten. For example, a pot of yoghurt may state 'sell by 12 March (4)', which means that it should be eaten by 16th March. Foods which stay at their best for up to 3 months carry a 'best before' date and the day and month. Those that stay fresh for up to 18 months carry a 'best before' date and the month and year, or a 'best before end' plus the month and year. Highly perishable foods will soon have 'use by' dates instead of 'sell by' dates. The 'use by' date will indicate when the food must be eaten by. If the date cannot be printed beside the words the consumer must be referred to another place, e.g. Best before: See date on lid.

It is not illegal to sell food that is past its datemark; it can still be sound and wholesome although no longer at its best. Often such items are reduced in price. However, it is illegal to sell food that has gone off or is unfit for consumption, even if it has not passed its datemark. Any conditions that must be followed in order to keep the food fresh must be included on the label, e.g. 'store in a cool dark place'.

The Weight

Until the late 1970s manufacturers had to print the minimum weight or volume likely to be present. For most foods the manufacturer must now state the average weight. By law packs are not permitted to be underweight by more than a small amount. The majority of foods may be packed to any weight the manufacturer chooses, but some foods have to be sold in specified amounts. Bread loaves have to be either less than 300 g (when the weight does not have to be declared) or 400 g or 800 g (when the weight must be declared). Packets of milk, tea, biscuits and butter all have specified weights. The only exceptions to declaring a weight, volume or the number in a pack are baked goods, ice lollies and water ices.

Name and Address

The name or business name and the address of

the manufacturer, packer or seller within the EC must appear on the label. This informs the consumer who is responsible for the original condition of the food, and who to contact for further information about the product.

Place of Origin

This must be provided if the consumer is likely to be misled by the name of a product. For example, the consumer would not expect all Eccles cakes to be made in Eccles, but they might reasonably expect all Devon fudge to be made in Devon.

Instructions for Use

Any special instructions for use must be given. For instance, certain fats can only be used for spreading and not for cooking. Instructions must also be given if it would be difficult to use the product properly without them, e.g. instructions for a cake mix, or a food that must be reheated in a microwave.

Nutrition Information

Although not required by law, many products carry nutrition information that in its simplest form gives the energy, protein, fat and carbo-hydrate content of the food. Additional infor-mation such as sugars, fibre, salt, vitamins and minerals, or a break down of fat into saturated, monounsaturated and polyunsaturated fatty acids, or carbohydrate into sugars and starch may also be given. Labels show the nutrient content per 100 g of the food sold. If the product contains less than 100 g of food the label may show the nutrient content of the whole pack, or of an individual serving.

There are various methods of providing the data, which often makes it difficult for the consumer to compare similar products. It would be preferable for nutrition information to be presented in a standard format.

Claims

A food that claims to be suitable for a particular group of people, e.g. diabetics or slimmers, must meet specific conditions. Slimming products must contain no more than 40 kcal or 175 kJ of energy per 100 g of food. A product that claims to be 'high in polyunsaturates' must meet certain conditions relating to the total amount of fat and the relative amounts of saturated and polyunsaturated fatty acids. These values must appear on the label. Specific conditions must also be met for a product that claims to be 'low in cholesterol' or 'contains vitamins and minerals'. Foods cannot claim to prevent or cure illness or disease; such a claim would legally classify it as a medicine and even stricter controls would then apply.

What To Look For When Buying Food

Read the labels carefully and check that the

product contains the ingredients that you approve of.

Avoid processed food with long lists of additives and where possible choose an additive-free brand, or the brand with the least additives.

Always check the datemark on food and buy the freshest.

Do not buy battered boxes, even if reduced, and never buy dented, rusty or blown (bulging ends) cans.

Check fresh fruit and vegetables for imperfections such as coloured blemishes, loss of texture, limp or wilted leaves, cuts and general colour.

Raw fish should be thoroughly chilled and there are obvious signs to look for to tell whether it is fresh: a bright and clear colour; shiny glistening skin; prominent eyes, pink or red gills, firm scales, a fresh smell (with no hint of ammonia); a stiff, rigid texture.

Red meat that is bright red in colour does not necessarily indicate good quality. The colour of cut meat can vary from bright red to dark brown, as exposure to the air discolours it. Many butchers use tinted lighting to enhance the colour of their meat. Any fat should be firm and not discoloured in any way.

Examine eggs for cracks, blemishes and soiling by droppings. Check the sell by dates to make sure of the freshest eggs.

Appendix II

Additive-Free Cooking

Storing Food

How food is cooked and stored is just as important as the kind of food you buy. Choosing more additive-free food may require some changes in how the food is bought and stored in the home.

Perishable, chilled and frozen foods must be transported home as soon as possible. It is a good idea to pack any chilled and frozen foods together, preferably in an insulated bag. Shopping should not be left in a warm car for hours.

Bags should be unpacked as soon as you get home. All foods requiring refrigeration and freezing should be unpacked first and the fridge and freezer filled up in one go. If you keep opening and shutting the door the temperature will rise above the recommended level.

It is important to follow carefully any storage advice given on the packaging. Increasingly, more products are made without the use of preservatives, such as bread and jam, and consequently their shelf life is much shorter, particularly in warm weather. Once opened pickles, jams and chutneys are best kept in the fridge. They can ferment in warm conditions and may even explode. Once mould has grown on jam it should be thrown away. Bread should not normally be kept in the fridge, but when it is warm and humid putting the bread in a polythene bag and then in the fridge will delay it from going mouldy. However, bread will go stale more quickly when stored this way. Alternatively, half the loaf may be frozen until required.

Free-range eggs sometimes have dirty shells, but they should never be washed before storage because this can transfer any organisms from the shell surface inside to the raw egg.

The temperature of domestic fridges should be below 5°C. To maintain this temperature fridges should be defrosted regularly, and it is also a good idea to occasionally check the temperature with a thermometer. Hot food should not be put straight into the fridge because this will raise the temperature; it should be covered after cooking and left to cool. It is also important that not too much food is piled up in the fridge because the air must be able to circulate freely for it to work efficiently.

To avoid the high risk of contamination with food poisoning, all cooked foods must be stored at the top of the fridge with uncooked foods below. The juices from raw meat or poultry must not be allowed to drip onto food which is not going to be cooked or re-heated in any way. To prevent cross-contamination and the food from drying out, individual items should be covered with foil or cling film, or placed in polythene bags or airtight containers.

The correct temperature for a domestic freezer is -20°C. Frozen foods do not keep indefinitely and the manufacturers' instructions must be followed. There are four categories of freezer, identified by different numbers of stars: a four-star freezer can be used to freeze fresh food; a three-star freezer can store ready-frozen food for up to three months; a two-star can store ready-frozen food for up to two months; a one-star for only one week. The freezer's handbook will provide instructions about home-prepared food. It is quite a useful idea to label bought frozen food with the date it was bought and the date by which it should have been used. Once food has been thawed out it must not be refrozen. Only refreeze if ice-crystals are still visible.

Canned, dried and unopened bottled goods can be stored in a cool, dry cupboard, preferably away from the fridge and cooker because they both give out a lot of heat. Stores of food should be rotated with the oldest at the front and newest at the back. It is important to keep a check on the datemark. Many of the store cupboard foods have long shelf lives, but it is all too easy to hoard items that are well past their best.

Cooking Food

A diet of predominantly home-prepared foods will contain little in the way of additives. Food prepared in the home is not intended to have a long shelf life, nor do the cooking methods employed usually destroy the colour and flavour of the food to any great extent.

The one additive that is used extensively in the kitchen is salt. It is generally accepted that too much salt is eaten in the UK, far more than the body actually needs. Although most of this salt comes from processed foods many people still add too much during cooking and at the table. Salt can easily be replaced in cooking by a more adventurous and experimental use of herbs and spices. They can be used in a great variety of ways and not just in the traditional partnerships of basil and tomatoes, mint and lamb and cloves and pork. Fresh and dried herbs can be sprinkled on meat and fish before grilling or roasting, and sprigs of herbs or whole, peeled onions placed inside poultry. There is a vast range of herbs and spices to try, which not only add their own flavours but also enhance those of the other ingredients. As well as herbs and spices, mustards, vinegar, lemon juice and garlic can all be used to avoid bland-tasting food.

The distinctive flavour of garlic can transform an ordinary dish into something quite special. As a flavouring it has a place in every savoury dish; fried in oil before stir-frying meat, with fish and vegetables, in soups, casseroles and stews, as well as in tomato and other sauces. Cloves of garlic can be pushed into small cuts in a leg of lamb, and rubbing a salad bowl with a clove can give a subtler flavour than using it in the dressing. Eating a little fresh parsley will usually remove the lingering smell of garlic on the breath.

Instead of putting the salt cellar on the table put alternatives such as different types of pepper (white, black or paprika), mustards (English, French, German and American), cumin or nutmeg.

If salt is not used in cooking, it is important to retain the natural flavours of food as much as possible. Vegetables should retain their crispness and not be over-cooked. Cooking vegetables for a shorter period of time will help to keep their flavour and appearance, as well as those nutrients susceptible to heat. The tradition of adding bicarbonate of soda to green vegetables, to give them a bright green colour, is an unfortunate one because it destroys vitamin C and the B complex vitamins. Often the simplest cooking methods are the best ways of retaining flavour.

Fish has a delicate flavour which can be easily destroyed by coating it with batter and then frying it at very high temperatures. Baking fish, in foil or grease-proof paper, will keep the full flavour of the fish. Marinading fish and meat tenderizes the flesh and so cuts down the cooking time, but it also provides an opportunity to add various additional flavours. A marinade consists of an acid (e.g. vinegar, lemon juice or wine), oil, herbs and spices. The combination of flavours that can be blended is endless, especially if the more unusual vegetable oils are used, such as walnut, sesame and hazelnut oil.

The advantage of processed foods are that they are convenient, easy to prepare and quick to cook. However, with a little effort and time additive-free foods can be prepared to replace them. Stock can be made by boiling up bones or vegetable peelings for use in casseroles, stews and soups, instead of using highly salted stock cubes which invariably have added flavouring and flavour enhancers. Home baking and bread-making can cut out many additives, although it may be necessary in some recipes to use a raising agent such as baking powder, bicarbonate of soda or yeast. Some cooking methods do not need to rely on such ingredients or additives. Sponge cakes rise because air is incorporated as the eggs and sugar are whisked over hot water, batters (e.g. Yorkshire pudding) rely on the conversion of water to steam to lift them. Breakfast cereals do not usually contain additives, but some do have high salt contents. An alternative would be a home-made muesli based on oats and other cereals.

Because of the decreasing use of preservatives and antioxidants it is important to thoroughly thaw and properly cook foods. The following guidelines should be adhered to:

1. Frozen foods should be allowed to thaw in the fridge or a cool room, or a microwave can be used. The food should be loosely covered to allow air to circulate. No ice crystals should remain before cooking, and with poultry it should be possible to move the legs.

2. The liquid that comes from the food as it thaws must never be used and it should be thrown away.

3. Food should be cooked as soon as possible after it has been thawed out.

4. Thawed food should only be refrozen if it has been thoroughly cooked first.

5. Previously frozen food must be reheated until it is 'piping hot'. Sauces should bubble and food should be too hot to eat immediately.

6. Food should not be reheated more than once, whether originally cooked at home or bought as a chilled product, and any leftovers must be thrown away.

Appendix III

Table of additive numbers, main chemical names and main functions

The following table lists the additives that have been designated numbers by the European Commission. The additives appear in numerical order, along with the major substance or substances that each number refers to. The third column gives the major function of that group. The A to Z section of this book lists these substances under their chemical names, and this table may be used to find the relevant A to Z entry if you only know the substance's numerical designation.

Number	Chemical name(s)	Main function(s)
E100	curcumin	colour
E101	riboflavin	colour
101a	riboflavin-5′-phosphate	colour
E102	tartrazine	colour
E104	quinoline yellow	colour

107	yellow 2G	colour
E110	sunset yellow FCF	colour
E120	cochineal	colour
E122	carmoisine	colour
E123	amaranth	colour
E124	ponceau 4R	colour
E127	erythrosine	colour
128	red 2G	colour
129	allura red AC	colour
E131	patent blue V	colour
E132	indigo carmine	colour
133	brilliant blue FCF	colour
E140	chlorophyll	colour
E141	copper complexes of chlorophyll and chlorophyllins	colour
E142	green S	colour
E150	caramel	colour
E151	black PN	colour
E153	carbon black	colour

Number	Chemical name(s)	Main function(s)
154	brown FK	colour
155	brown HT	colour
E160a	alpha-carotene, beta-carotene, carotene and gamma-carotene	colour
E160b	annatto	colour
E160c	capsanthin	colour
E160d	lycopene	colour
E160e	beta-apo-8'-carotenal	colour
E160f	ethyl ester of beta apo-8'-carotenoic acid	colour
E161	xanthophylls	colour
E161a	flavoxanthin	colour
E161b	lutein	colour
E161c	cryptoxanthin	colour
E161d	rubixanthin	colour
E161e	violoxanthin	colour

E161f	rhodoxanthin	colour
E161g	canthaxanthin	colour
E162	beetroot red	colour
E163	anthocyanins	colour
E163a	cyanadin	colour
E163b	delphinidin	colour
E170	calcium carbonate	base firming agent, release agent, diluent, and surface food colourant and nutrient in flour
E171	titanium dioxide	colour
E172	iron oxides, iron hydroxides	colour
E173	aluminium	surface colour
E174	silver	surface colour
E175	gold	surface colour
E180	pigment rubine	colour
E200	sorbic acid	preservative
E201	sodium sorbate	preservative
E202	potassium sorbate	preservative
E203	calcium sorbate	preservative

Number	Chemical name(s)	Main function(s)
E210	benzoic acid	preservative
E211	sodium benzoate	preservative
E212	potassium benzoate	preservative
E213	calcium benzoate	preservative
E214	ethyl 4-hydroxybenzoate	preservative
E215	ethyl 4-hydroxybenzoate, sodium salt	preservative
E216	propyl 4-hydroxybenzoate	preservative
E217	propyl 4-hydroxybenzoate, sodium salt	preservative
E218	methyl 4-hydroxybenzoate	preservative
E219	methyl 4-hydroxybenzoate, sodium salt	preservative
E220	sulphur dioxide	preservative
E221	sodium sulphite	preservative
E222	sodium hydrogen sulphite	preservative

E223	sodium metabisulphite	preservative
E224	potassium metabisulphite	preservative
E226	calcium sulphite	preservative
E227	calcium hydrogen sulphite	preservative
E230	biphenyl	preservative
E231	2-hydroxybiphenyl	preservative
E232	sodium biphenyl-2-yloxide	preservative
E233	2-(thiazol-4-yl) benzimidazole	preservative
234	nisin	preservative
E236	formic acid	preservative
E237	sodium formate	preservative
E238	calcium formate	preservative
E239	hexamine	preservative
E249	potassium nitrite	preservative
E250	sodium nitrite	preservative
E251	sodium nitrate	preservative
E252	potassium nitrate	preservative

Number	Chemical name(s)	Main function(s)
E260	acetic acid	acidity regulator, buffer, preservative, flavouring, diluent
E261	potassium acetate	colour preserver, acidity regulator, buffer
E262	sodium hydrogen diacetate	acidity regulator, sequestrant, preservative
262	sodium acetate (anhydrous) and sodium acetate	buffer
E263	calcium acetate	anti-mould agent, sequestrant, firming agent, stabilizer, buffer
E270	lactic acid	preservative, acid, flavouring
E280	propionic acid	preservative
E281	sodium propionate	preservative
E282	calcium propionate	preservative

E283	potassium propionate	preservative
E290	carbon dioxide	preservative, coolant, freezant, packaging gas aerator
296	malic acid (DL- or L-)	acid, flavouring
297	fumaric acid	acid, flavouring, raising agent, antioxidant
E300	ascorbic acid	antioxidant, flour improver, anti-browning agent
E301	sodium L-ascorbate	antioxidant, colour preserver
E302	calcium L-ascorbate	antioxidant, colour preserver
E304	6-O-palmitoyl-L-ascorbic acid	antioxidant, flour improver, anti-browning agent
E306	tocopherols, in extracts of natural origin	antioxidant
E307	synthetic alpha-tocopherol	antioxidant

Number	Chemical name(s)	Main function(s)
E308	synthetic gamma-tocopherol	antioxidant
E309	synthetic delta-tocopherol	antioxidant
E310	propyl gallate	antioxidant
E311	octyl gallate	antioxidant
E312	dodecyl gallate	antioxidant
E320	butylated hydroxyanisole	antioxidant
E321	butylated hydroxytoluene	antioxidant
E322	lecithins	emulsifier, antioxidant
E325	sodium lactate	antioxidant synergist, humectant, bulking agent
E326	potassium lactate	antioxidant synergist, acidity regulator
E327	calcium lactate	antioxidant, buffer, firming agent, yeast food, dough conditioner

E330	citric acid	antioxidant, acidifier, sequestrant, flavouring agent
E331	sodium citrates	buffer, emulsifier, sequestrant
E331a	sodium dihydrogen citrate	buffer, emulsifier, sequestrant
E331b	disodium citrate	antioxidant, buffer, emulsifying salt
E331c	trisodium citrate	antioxidant, buffer, emulsifying salt, seqestrant, stabilizer
E332	potassium dihydrogen citrate and tripotassium citrate	buffer, emulsifying salt, yeast food
E333	Mono-, di-, and tricalcium citrate	buffer, firming agent, emulsifying salt, sequestrant, flour improver
E334	L-(+)-tartaric acid	antioxidant, sequestrant, diluent

Number	Chemical name(s)	Main function(s)
E335	monosodium L-(+)-tartrate and disodium L-(+)-tartrate	antioxidant, synergist, buffer, emulsifying salt, sequestrant
E336	monopotassium-L-(+)-tartrate and dipotassium L-(+)-tartrate	acid, buffer, raising agent, synergist, antioxidant, emulsifying salt
E337	potassium sodium L-(+)-tartrate	buffer, emulsifying salt, stabilizer, synergist
E338	orthophosphoric acid	synergist, acidulant, flavouring agent
E339a	sodium dihydrogen orthophosphate	buffer, sequestrant
E339b	disodium hydrogen orthophosphate	buffer, sequestrant
E339c	trisodium orthophosphate	buffer, sequestrant
E340a	potassium dihydrogen orthophosphate	buffer, sequestrant

E340b	dipotassium hydrogen orthophosphate	buffer, sequestrant
E340c	tripotassium orthophosphate	buffer, sequestrant
E341	calcium orthophosphates	firming agent, anti-caking agent, raising agent
E341a	calcium tetrahydrogen diorthophosphate	buffer, yeast food, sequestrant, texturizer
E341b	calcium hydrogen orthophosphate	yeast food, dough conditioner, emulsifier, sequestrant
E341c	tricalcium diorthophosphate	anti-caking agent, yeast food, firming agent, buffer
350	sodium malate and sodium hydrogen malate	buffer, humectant, seasoning agent
351	potassium malate	buffer, seasoning agent
352	calcium malate and calcium hydrogen malate	buffer, firming agent, seasoning agent
353	metatartaric acid	acidifier, antioxidant synergist, sequestrant

Number	Chemical name(s)	Main function(s)
355	adipic acid	buffer, acidulating agent, flavouring agent, raising agent
363	succinic acid	acid, buffer, neutralizing agent
370	1,4-heptonolactone	sequestrant, acid
375	nicotinic acid	vitamin supplement, colour preserver
380	triammonium citrate	buffer, emulsifying salt, softening agent
381	ammonium ferric citrate and ammonium ferric citrate, green	dietary supplement
385	calcium disodium ethylenediamine-tetra-acetate	chelating agent, antioxidant synergist, sequestrant, preservative
E400	alginic acid	thickening agent, stabilizer

E401	sodium alginate	thickening agent, stabilizer
E402	potassium alginate	thickening agent, stabilizer
E403	ammonium alginate	stabilizer, emulsifier and thickener
E404	calcium alginate	thickening agent, stabilizer
E405	alginate ester	thickening agent, stabilizer, defoaming agent
E406	agar	thickening agent, stabilizer, gelling agent, humectant
E407	carrageenan	stabilizer, thickening agent, suspending agent, gelling agent
E408	furcellaran	thickening agent, gelling agent, stabilizer

Number	Chemical name(s)	Main function(s)
E410	locust bean gum	gelling agent, stabilizer, emulsifier, thickening agent
E412	guar gum	thickening agent, stabilizer, suspending agent, bulking agent
E413	tragacanth	emulsifier, stabilizer, thickening agent
E414	gum arabic	thickening agent, emulsifier, stabilizer
E415	xanthan gum	stabilizer, thickening agent, emulsifier
416	karaya gum	stabilizer, thickening agent, emulsifier
E420i	sorbitol	sweetening agent, humectant, sequestrant, texturizer

E420ii	sorbitol syrup	sweetening agent, humectant, sequestrant, texturizer
E421	mannitol	texturizing agent, sweetening agent, humectant, anti-caking agent, anti-sticking agent
E422	glycerol	humectant, solvent
430	polyoxyethylene (8) stearate	emulsifier, stabilizer
431	polyoxyethylene (40) stearate	emulsifier
432	polyoxyethylene (20) sorbitan monolaurate	emulsifier, stabilizer, dispersing agent
433	polyoxyethylene (20) sorbitan mono-oleate	emulsifier, defoaming agent, stabilizer
434	polyoxyethylene (20) sorbitan monopalmitate	emulsifier, stabilizer, dispersing, defoaming and wetting agent
435	polyoxyethylene (20) sorbitan monostearate	emulsifier, stabilizer, wetting and dispersing agent

Number	Chemical name(s)	Main function(s)
436	polyoxyethylene (20) sorbitan tristearate	emulsifier, stabilizer, wetting and dispersing agent
E440a	pectin	emulsifier, thickening agent, gelling agent, stabilizer
E440b	amidated pectin	emulsifier, stabilizer, gelling and thickening agent
442	ammonium phosphatides	stabilizer, emulsifier
E450a	disodium dihydrogen diphosphate, trisodium diphosphate, tetrasodium diphosphate and tetrapotassium diphosphate	buffer, sequestrant, raising agent, colour improver, chelating agent
E450b	pentasodium triphosphate and pentapotassium triphosphate	emulsifying salt, texturizer, buffer, sequestrant, stabilizer

E450c	sodium polyphosphates and potassium polyphosphates	emulsifying salt, sequestrant, stabilizer, texturizer
E460a	microcrystalline cellulose	bulking agent, binder, anti-caking agent, stabilizer
E460b	alpha cellulose	bulking agent, binder, anti-caking agent, stabilizer
E461	methylcellulose	emulsifier, stabilizer, thickening, bulking and binding agent
E463	hydroxypropylcellulose	stabilizer, emulsifier and thickening agent
E464	hydroxypropylmethylcellulose	gelling agent, emulsifier, stabilizer, thickening agent
E465	ethylmethylcellulose	emulsifier, foam stabilizer, thickening and suspending agent

Number	Chemical name(s)	Main function(s)
E466	carboxymethylcellulose	thickening agent, texture modifier, stabilizer, gelling and bulking agent, foam stabilizer
E470	sodium, potassium and calcium salts of fatty acids	emulsifier, stabilizer, anti-caking agent
E471	mono- and diglycerides of fatty acids	emulsifier, stabilizer, thickening agent
E472a	acetic acid esters of mono- and di-glcerides of fatty acids	emulsifier, stabilizer, coating agent, texture modifying agent, solvent, lubricant
E472b	lactic acid esters of mono- and diglycerides of fatty acids	emulsifier, stabilizer
E472c	citric acid esters of mono- and diglycerides of fatty acids	emulsifier, stabilizer

E472d	tartaric acid esters of mono- and diglycerides of fatty acids	emulsifier, stabilizer
E472e	mono- and di-acetyltartaric acid esters of mono- and diglycerides of fatty acids	emulsifier, stabilizer
E473	sucrose esters of fatty acids	emulsifier, stabilizer
E474	sucroglycerides	emulsifier, stabilizer
E475	polyglycerol esters of fatty acids	emulsifier, stabilizer
476	polyglycerol esters of polycondensed fatty acids of castor oil	emulsifier, stabilizer
E477	propane-1,2-diol esters of fatty acids	emulsifier, stabilizer
478	lactylated fatty acid esters of glycerol and propane-1,2-diol	emulsifier, stabilizer, whipping agent, plasticizer, surface active agent
E481	sodium stearoyl-2 lactylate	emulsifier, stabilizer
E482	calcium stearoyl-2-lactylate	emulsifier, stabilizer, whipping agent
E483	stearyl tartrate	emulsifier, stabilizer, flour treatment agent

Number	Chemical name(s)	Main function(s)
491	sorbitan monostearate	emulsifier, stabilizer, glazing agent
492	sorbitan tristearate	emulsifier, stabilizer
493	sorbitan monolaurate	emulsifier, stabilizer, anti-foaming agent
494	sorbitan mono-oleate	emulsifier, stabilizer
495	sorbitan monopalmitate	emulsifier, stabilizer
500	sodium carbonate, sodium hydrogen carbonate and sodium sesquicarbonate	base, aerating agent, diluent
501	potassium carbonate and potassium hydrogen carbonate	base, alkali
503	ammonium carbonate and ammonium hydrogen carbonate	buffer, neutralizing agent, leavening, aerating and raising agent
504	magnesium carbonate	alkali, anti-caking agent, acidity regulator, anti-bleaching agent

507	hydrochloric acid	acid
508	potassium chloride	gelling agent, salt substitute
509	calcium chloride	sequestrant, firming agent
510	ammonium chloride	yeast food, flavour
513	sulphuric acid	acid
514	sodium sulphate	diluent
515	potassium sulphate	salt substitute
516	calcium sulphate	firming agent, sequestrant, nutrient, yeast food, excipient
518	magnesium sulphate	dietary supplement, firming agent
524	sodium hydroxide	base, colour solvent
525	potassium hydroxide	base, oxidizing agent
525	calcium hydroxide	firming agent, neutralizing agent

Number	Chemical name(s)	Main function(s)
527	ammonium hydroxide	colour diluent, colour solvent, alkali
528	magnesium hydroxide	alkali
529	calcium oxide	alkali, processing aid
530	magnesium oxide	anti-caking agent, alkali
535	sodium ferrocyanide	anti-caking agent
536	potassium ferrocyanide	anti-caking agent
540	dicalcium diphosphate	yeast food, dough conditioner, dietary supplement, neutralizing agent
541	sodium aluminium phosphate, acidic and sodium aluminium phosphate, basic	raising agent, emulsifying salt
542	edible bone phosphate	anti-caking agent, mineral supplement
544	calcium polyphosphates	emulsifier, firming agent, sequestrant

545	ammonium polyphosphates	emulsifier, emulsifying salt, sequestrant, yeast food, stabilizer
551	silicon dioxide	suspending agent, anti-caking agent, thickening agent, stabilizer
552	calcium silicate	anti-caking agent, glazing, polishing, releasing, dusting, coating and suspending agent
553a	magnesium silicate, synthetic and magnesium trisilicate	anti-caking, glazing, polishing, releasing and dusting agent
553b	talc	releasing and anti caking agent, filtering aid, dusting powder
554	aluminium sodium silicate	anti-caking agent
556	aluminium calcium silicate	anti-caking agent

Number	Chemical name(s)	Main function(s)
558	bentonite	anti-caking agent, clarifying agent, filtration aid, suspending and emulsifying agent
559	kaolin, heavy and kaolin, light	anti-caking and clarifying agent
570	stearic acid	anti-caking agent
572	magnesium stearate	anti-caking agent, emulsifier, release agent
575	D-glucono-1,5-lactone	acid, sequestrant
576	sodium gluconate	sequestrant, dietary supplement
577	potassium gluconate	sequestrant
578	calcium gluconate	buffer, firming agent, sequestrant
620	L-glutamic acid	dietary supplement, flavour enhancer, salt substitute

621	monosodium glutamate	flavour enhancer
622	potassium hydrogen L-glutamate	flavour enhancer, salt substitute
623	calcium dihydrogen di-L-glutamate	flavour enhancer, salt substitute
627	guanosine 5'-(disodium phosphate)	flavour enhancer
631	inosine 5'-(disodium phosphate)	flavour enhancer
635	sodium 5'-ribonucleotide	flavour enhancer
636	maltol	flavouring agent, flavour enhancer
637	ethyl maltol	flavouring agent, flavour enhancer
900	dimethylpolysiloxane	water repellant, anti-foaming and anti-caking agent
901	beeswax, white, and beeswax, yellow	glazing, polishing and releasing agent
903	carnauba wax	glazing and polishing agent

Number	Chemical name(s)	Main function(s)
904	shellac	glazing and polishing agent
905	mineral hydrocarbons	polishing, glazing, sealing, defoaming and release agent
907	refined microcrystalline wax	polishing, release and stiffening agent
920	L-cysteine hydrochloride and L-cysteine hydrochloride monohydrate	improving agent in flour, flavour
924	potassium bromate	improving agent
925	chlorine	preservative, bleaching, and oxidizing agent
926	chlorine dioxide	improving and oxidizing agent
927	azodicarbonamide	flour improver